DARWIN AND HIS CRITICS

Wadsworth Guides to Literary Study

Maurice Beebe, General Editor

DARWIN AND HIS CRITICS
The Darwinian Revolution
   edited by Bernard R. Kogan, University of Illinois, Chicago

LITERARY SYMBOLISM
An Introduction to the Interpretation of Literature
   edited by Maurice Beebe, Purdue University

A *SCARLET LETTER* HANDBOOK
   edited by Seymour L. Gross, University of Notre Dame

THE *KING LEAR* PERPLEX
   edited by Helmut Bonheim, University of California, Santa Barbara

CONRAD'S *HEART OF DARKNESS* AND THE CRITICS
   edited by Bruce Harkness, University of Illinois

DARWIN
AND HIS CRITICS

The Darwinian Revolution

Edited by Bernard R. Kogan
University of Illinois (Chicago)

WADSWORTH PUBLISHING COMPANY, INC.
SAN FRANCISCO

L.C. Cat. Card No.: 60-9980

Printed in the United States of
America.

Manufactured by American Book–
Stratford Press, Inc.

PREFACE

My aim in this book has been to assemble a representative selection of writings related to the theories developed in the second half of the nineteenth century by the great British naturalists Charles Robert Darwin and Alfred Russel Wallace. These theories, which collectively constitute "Darwinism" and which launched the "Darwinian Revolution," were designed expressly to account for one of the most significant intellectual conceptions of all time—biological evolution—but their influence has been more widely felt in almost every phase of human activity.

The effect of Darwinism on the literature of the nineteenth and twentieth centuries has been so great that Western intellectual traditions cannot be fully understood without some knowledge of it. To introduce Darwinism, I have supplied excerpts from the writings of Darwin and Wallace on the theory of "natural selection," the principal ingredient of Darwinism, and parts of the written criticisms of Darwinism which best reflect its changing fortunes during the past century.

I have approached this engrossing subject not as a practicing biologist—which I am not—but as a student of Victorian thought and expression in England and America. As a nonspecialist, I have collected these readings for the interested nonspecialist student or reader-at-large. *Darwin and His Critics* is designed especially for students of English composition, of Victorian and twentieth century literature and society, and of the history of ideas. It is not a book about evolution, natural selection, or genetics. The fact is that evolution and the theories of Darwin and Wallace transcend the merely scientific. Only those writings which are specifically concerned with Darwinism are presented. On only one or two occasions—as, for example, in the brief passage by Thomas H. Morgan explaining his chromosome theory—have I included anything that bears only tangentially on Darwinism. In all other instances, the bearing is direct and firsthand. I have also deliberately avoided the extremely difficult works of the mathematical biologists of our day, with the exception of a brief nontechnical selection from Sir Ronald A. Fisher.

In the Introduction, I have attempted to place Darwinism in its historical setting and to recount in brief detail the circumstances surrounding the origins of the Darwinian Revolution. The principal concepts are explained as clearly and as succinctly as possible. The summaries preceding each of the major sections of the book are intended to serve as sub-introductions and transitions. Biographical and explanatory footnotes are provided wherever needed. The Glossary contains definitions of biological and geological terms, brief biographical statements on each of the contributors to *Darwin and His Critics* as well as on other important persons mentioned in this book, and a table of geological time.

The two appendixes are meant to throw particularly revealing literary and historical light on the subject. In the first, George Bernard Shaw, unquenchable fount of wit and wisdom on most matters of interest to man, expounds on evolution and Darwinism in his Preface to *Back to Methuselah*. The second contains excerpts from the sensational Tennessee Evolution Trial, or Scopes Trial, of 1925, which now seems, in retrospect, like the last gasp of religious Fundamentalism in its battle with Evolution—a kind of folk epic of Evolution on Trial.

Darwin and His Critics is self-contained in terms of what it sets out to do, but the reader will need to move outside the text and into the library for a fuller understanding of the subject. I have indicated in the bibliographical essay entitled "Suggestions for Further Study" three areas of outside reading and research: (1) the specific field of organic evolution and biological Darwinism, (2) the application of Darwinism to the social sciences—what is commonly referred to as "Social Darwinism," and (3) the influence of Darwinism on the imaginative literature of the nineteenth and twentieth centuries.

The last section of the book contains questions and suggested topics for short investigative papers on each of the book's divisions, as well as questions and suggestions for long papers based on the complete book. The questions are intended to help readers gain maximum returns from their reading. The suggested topics have been devised particularly for the student who is learning the techniques of research. Teachers may find various uses for this book; it can serve as a basis for the assignment of either short essays or term reports, and perhaps both in sequence. Writing long or short papers will expose the student to the disciplines involved in documented research: planning and outlining; preparing notecards and bibliography cards and, from them, footnotes and bibliography; and learning the uses of direct quotation and paraphrase.

Within each of the major parts of the book the readings are arranged chronologically according to the dates of first publication. Here and there, and for the sake of clarity, I have taken a few minor liberties in reproducing chapter and section titles, but all variations in spelling and punctuation have been retained. A complete biographical entry appears before every selection, and page numbers from the original sources are given in raised brackets. When a page in the original text ends with part of a word, I have placed the page reference at the end of the completed word.

PREFACE

I should like to record my gratitude for their co-operation and direction to the staffs of the Newberry Library of Chicago (and to Ben Bowman, in particular), the John Crerar Library of Chicago, and the libraries of Northwestern and Roosevelt Universities and of the Universities of Chicago and Illinois (Chicago). For helpful advice and instruction, I am also deeply grateful to Dr. Theodor Just, Curator of Botany of the Chicago Natural History Museum.

B. R. Kogan
Chicago, November 1959

To My Mother
and
The Memory of My Father

CONTENTS

Part One

The Sources of the Darwinian Revolution

THE LINNEAN SOCIETY PAPERS OF 1858:

CHARLES DARWIN:

Part Two

Early Defenders of Darwinism

JOSEPH D. HOOKER:

INTRODUCTION

The independent co-formulation of the theory of natural selection by Charles Darwin and Alfred Wallace, however unlikely it may seem in retrospect, is by now a familiar monument in the intellectual history of man. From the various accounts that we have of the details of the discovery and of its public announcement on July 1, 1858, at a meeting of the Linnean Society of London, the facts in the case have become clear. All the principals involved—the theorists as well as their sponsors —agree on what actually happened.

It was Sir Charles Lyell, the most distinguished geologist of his day in England, and Joseph D. Hooker, one of Britain's leading botanists, who prevailed upon Darwin to have read before the Society, under their joint sponsorship, a portion of what would eventually be published as *On the Origin of Species by Means of Natural Selection, or the Preservation of Favoured Races in the Struggle for Life.* Wallace's paper on variation, entitled *On the Tendency of Varieties to depart indefinitely from the Original Type,* was also read at the same meeting.

The story of how Darwin and Wallace, unknown to one another, came to formulate the same evolutionary theory, Darwin after many years of experimentation and gathering of evidence and Wallace in a much shorter space of time, was later recounted by each man. Each spoke generously of the other, and the relationship between them continued to be cordial. Some champions of Wallace occasionally resented the fact that very soon after the publication of *The Origin of Species* in 1859, Darwinism became almost synonymous with "natural selection" [1] (if not, indeed, with "evolution" itself); some even proposed "Wallaceism" as a possible and worthy variant. But Wallace throughout his life took pains to acknowledge the priority of Darwin's investigations and to pay tribute to Darwin's greatness as a naturalist. And though he disagreed with Darwin on some matters, he continued to support natural selection in the name of Darwinism.

When Darwin and Wallace startled the world with their concep-

---

[1] It has been so used, in fact, throughout this Introduction, as well as in the editor's Preface. The reader is cautioned, however, that Darwinism in its largest application embraces other Darwinian concepts such as "pangenesis"—Darwin's theory of the mechanism of hereditary transmission—and "sexual selection," in addition to natural selection.

tion of natural selection, most scientists and laymen believed in the "immutability" of species of plants and animals. According to this belief, specific types of living things are independently and "specially" created by God; and although they either persist from age to age or become extinct, they never undergo any significant physical change that makes them different from what they were when originally created. They are immutable—unchanged and unchangeable.

From antiquity there were those who took the opposite position and argued in support of organic evolution. They held that living things are *not* independently created but are mutable or transmutable —that is, capable of change or transformation—and evolve from one form to another through a process of what would later be called "descent by modification." At various stages of scientific history, proponents of this view, identified as "transmutationists" or defenders of the "derivative theory," worked out their particular conceptions of evolution. The most important transmutationist precursor of Darwin and Wallace was unquestionably the French naturalist Lamarck. In the eighteenth century, he formulated a theory of evolution fundamentally similar to the theories of Darwin and Wallace. But, although Lamarckism (as Lamarck's views came to be identified) was evolutionary or transmutationist, it also included a number of principles that Darwin and Wallace, in varying degrees, rejected and that most modern biologists reject. For example, Lamarck maintained that not only inborn but also acquired characteristics can be transmitted by heredity from parent to offspring. He also believed that changes in physical form can occur as the result of conscious willing on the part of the living beings experiencing these changes. Lamarckism has had its champions, but these two arguments are now almost universally denied by reputable students of evolution.

The important distinction between organic evolution and natural selection is thus made clear. Lamarck, Darwin, and Wallace were all evolutionists or transmutationists, but Darwin and Wallace believed in natural selection as the principal explanation of the mechanics of evolution. It was possible in 1859—as it is today—to accept evolution but not natural selection by subscribing to Lamarckism or to some other body of evolutionary theory.

The theory of Darwin and Wallace inaugurated what has been called "The Darwinian Revolution"—a disturbance and, for many, a destruction of previously unquestioned and cherished beliefs. A reaffirmation of the evolutionary principle, together with the formulation of a seemingly defensible explanation of its operation, necessarily came into conflict with the literal account of creation contained in the book of Genesis. Religious orthodoxy was shaken. For many, a familiar, comfortable, and secure body of faith was on the verge of being undermined. What many considered crass materialism or even atheism was apparently threatening to supplant idealism and devotion to an omniscient deity. The traditional belief in the divine government of human activity seemed menaced by a new faith in physical, natural laws—such as those of the "struggle for existence" and the "survival of the fittest"—which seemed nowhere to allow for supernatural intervention.

Under the circumstances, therefore, it is not surprising that the reception accorded *The Origin of Species* by press, clergy, and even the world of science was predominantly hostile. But Darwin was also blessed with dedicated, articulate, and influential defenders. In addition to Wallace, chief among these were Lyell and Hooker. After long discussions with Darwin, and especially after reading the Linnean Society Papers of 1858 and *The Origin of Species* a year later, both of these scientists came to believe that species were mutable and did not originate by special creation. They came to believe, in other words, in the theory of organic evolution or descent by modification, though, like Darwin himself, they would continue to doubt the all-sufficiency of natural selection to account for such transmutation.

Lyell's conversion to the doctrine of biological mutability was not altogether unexpected, for it was he who had argued in favor of the concept of "uniformitarianism" to explain geological change. According to Lyell's view, the earth is millions of years older than has commonly been supposed, old enough to have undergone slow, gradual changes in its crust. And the natural processes which accounted for these changes in the past were the same as those which cause similar changes in the present. The prevailing theory in Lyell's day was that of "catastrophism." Predicated on estimates that the earth was much younger, this theory held that geological changes are the result of periodic, sudden catastrophes, rather than slow, imperceptible modifications. As has often been pointed out, Lyell's uniformitarianism, worked out in his *Principles of Geology* (1830-33), prepared the way for Darwin's natural selection in the sense that it postulated the great age of the earth and the process of gradual change. Lyell had in effect reasserted the theory of *inorganic* evolution as opposed to catastrophism; Darwin's conception of natural selection supported the theory of *organic* evolution as opposed to that of the special creation of new species.

Thomas H. Huxley came to be the best known and most persistent of Darwin's defenders. Indeed, though he became distinguished in his own right as a biologist, author, and public speaker, he was widely known as "Darwin's bulldog," the propagandist and belligerent contender for Darwinism in the press and on the public platform. Although Huxley actually never accepted natural selection *in toto,* he nevertheless fought for it enthusiastically, especially when opposed by the clergy. The opening shot of the Darwinian Revolution may in fact be said to have been fired when Huxley delivered his celebrated retort to the Rev. Samuel Wilberforce, Bishop of Oxford. The story has been told many times by many people, but it deserves at least one more retelling on this centennial occasion:

At a meeting of the British Association for the Advancement of Science at Oxford University on June 30, 1860, which Huxley attended, Bishop Wilberforce had come close to the end of a violent attack on Darwin and *The Origin of Species* when he turned to Huxley and asked, sardonically, whether it was from his grandmother or grandfather that he claimed descent from an ape. Huxley saw his opening, waited for his turn to respond, and, after answering the Bishop's scientific objections incisively and convincingly, he asserted—according to the eye-witness account of an Oxford undergraduate—

that a man has no reason to be ashamed of having an ape for his grandfather. If there were an ancestor whom I should feel shame in recalling, it would be a *man*, a man of restless and versatile intellect, who, not content with an equivocal success in his own sphere of activity, plunges into scientific questions with which he has no real acquaintance, only to obscure them by an aimless rhetoric, and distract the attention of his hearers from the real point at issue by eloquent digressions, and skilled appeals to religious prejudice.[2]

This masterthrust not only won over Huxley's immediate audience, which was originally neutral or hostile to evolution and natural selection, but also marked the real beginning of Huxley's lifelong fight in support of Darwin and Darwinism.

The vogue for Darwinism was quickly established despite the formidable opposition to it in high places. Before his death in 1882, Darwin could say with assurance that no scientist of any standing clung to a belief in special creation; evolution had won the day—in terms of natural selection or of some comparable theory. But before the end of the century, Darwinians were fighting among themselves, "Neo-Darwinians" against "Neo-Lamarckians," though they all continued to pledge allegiance to Darwin. By the beginning of the twentieth century, Darwinism had been considerably modified and, with the advent of the science of genetics, would be modified even further. The modifications have in fact continued on into our own Nuclear Age, but Darwinism—according to the testimony of most reputable naturalists—remains today a vital and meaningful explanation of organic evolution.

~~~~~

[2] The undergraduate responsible for this account was John Richard Green. Huxley said that Green had captured the substance of his speech accurately, but that he doubted having used the word "equivocal." Other versions of what Huxley actually said differ somewhat from Green's, but they all amount to substantially the same thing. See Leonard Huxley, *Life and Letters of Thomas Henry Huxley* (London: Macmillan and Co., 1900), I, 179-189.

As this Introduction is being written, nearly fifty of the world's greatest scientists are meeting at the University of Chicago in an historic five-day Darwin Centennial Celebration (November 24-28, 1959) marking the hundredth anniversary of the publication of *The Origin of Species*. No attempt will be made here to summarize the proceedings of this distinguished group, but readers may be interested to know that the complete Centennial Celebration papers and panel discussions will be published in 1960 by the University of Chicago Press in a three-volume work entitled *Evolution After Darwin*.

Among the prominent men and women attending the Celebration are Sir Charles Darwin, grandson of the author of *The Origin of Species* and an eminent physicist and mathematician in his own right, and Sir Julian Huxley, grandson of Thomas H. Huxley and one of the foremost biologists of our time. In newspaper interviews and in radio and television appearances, as well as in their contributions to the Celebration, these men have discussed the present and future states of evolution, of Darwinism, and of man; and some of their views, in capsule form, may be appropriately stated here.

Both are agreed that evolution is no longer a tentative theory, but an established fact. Further, they believe that natural selection has now more or less ceased to operate as far as the physical evolution of man is concerned. Medical science allows us to treat and keep alive persons with pernicious mutations who would otherwise—that is, in terms of natural selection and the concept of "survival of the fittest"— be left to die. At the present time, man no longer has to evolve in any significant *physical* way in order to survive.

But both men are fearful of two catastrophes that threaten mankind. The first of these is nuclear destruction, which is now no longer a vague threat but a frightening possibility. The second is the growing population problem. Even if man is spared nuclear destruction, they say, he will eventually be faced by an acute shortage of food and living space, as a consequence of the population "explosions" occurring throughout the world. The rising world birth rate (presently estimated at more than 100,000 births daily) and falling death rate have produced a rate of increase that will more than double the world's present population by the end of the century.

Sir Charles fears that voluntary population control will fail and that someday the world's productive capacity will be overmatched by the sheer number of mouths to be fed. At such a time, he believes, Darwin's natural selection in its elemental form will once more begin to operate, and men will literally fight with one another for food. The stronger or otherwise more adaptable will survive and the less adaptable will perish.

Sir Julian is hopeful that, with the voluntary control of population increase, some point of stability may yet be reached before the planet swarms with many billions of inhabitants. In a Centennial Celebration address entitled "The Evolutionary Vision," Sir Julian reaffirmed his belief in evolution and argued that evolution has by this time impinged on every aspect of life. Man's future evolutionary development, he said, will be "psycho-social" and cultural, rather than physical. Man, uniquely possessed of rationality with which to work out his *own* destiny, is now capable of continued "human" evolution. If he eliminates the threats of nuclear self-destruction and uncontrollable population growth, and if he establishes an effective world government, he will then be free to guide the further evolution of his mind.

PART ONE

THE SOURCES OF THE DARWINIAN REVOLUTION

In response to the appeals of Sir Charles Lyell and Joseph Hooker, his friends and fellow-scientists, Darwin agreed that an extract from his manuscript work on species might be read at a meeting of the Linnean Society of London on July 1, 1858. Also read to the Society were Alfred Russel Wallace's essay explaining his conception of natural selection, and extracts from a letter written by Darwin in 1857 to Asa Gray, Professor of Botany at Harvard University, outlining the principles of his hypothesis. Prompted to complete an "abstract" of the comprehensive volume he had originally planned, Darwin published *The Origin of Species* on November 24, 1859. In 1871, after producing a number of significant books and articles on evolution, he published *The Descent of Man, and Selection in Relation to Sex.* The leading principles of Darwinism were chiefly derived from these two works.

The Linnean Society Papers of 1858

From *"On the Tendency of Species to form Varieties;* and *on the Perpetuation of Varieties and Species by Natural Means of Selection.* By CHARLES DARWIN, Esq., F.R.S., F.L.S., & F.G.S., and ALFRED WALLACE, Esq., Communicated by Sir CHARLES LYELL, F.R.S., F.L.S., and J. D. HOOKER, Esq., M.D., V.P.R.S., F.L.S., & (Read July 1, 1858.)" In *Journal of the Proceedings of the Linnean Society,* Zoology III (August 20, 1858), 45-62.

London, June 30th, 1858

MY DEAR SIR,—The accompanying papers, which we have the honour of communicating to the Linnean Society, and which all relate to the same subject, viz. the Laws which affect the Production of Varieties, Races, and Species, contain the results of the investigations of two indefatigable naturalists, Mr. Charles Darwin and Mr. Alfred Wallace.

These gentlemen having independently and unknown to one another, conceived the same very ingenious theory to account for the appearance and perpetuation of varieties and of specific forms on our planet, may both fairly claim the merit of being original thinkers in this important line of inquiry; but neither of them having published his views, though Mr. Darwin has for many years past been repeatedly urged by us to do so, and both authors having now unreservedly placed their papers in our hands, we think it would best promote the interests of science that a selection from them should be laid before the Linnean Society.

Taken in the order of their dates, they consist of:—

1. Extracts from a MS. work on Species,[1] by Mr. Darwin, which was sketched in 1839, and copied in 1844, when the copy was read by Dr. Hooker, and its contents afterwards communicated to Sir Charles Lyell. The first Part is devoted to "The Variation of Organic Beings under Domestication and in their Natural State;" and the second chapter of that Part, from which we propose to read to the Society the extracts referred to, is headed, "On the Variation of Organic Beings in a State

---

[1] This MS. work was never intended for publication, and therefore was not written with care. [Darwin's note in 1858.]

9

of Nature; on the Natural Means of Selection; and on the Comparisons of Domestic Races and true Species."

2. An abstract of a private letter addressed to Professor Asa Gray, of Boston, U.S., in October 1857, by Mr. Darwin, in which [45] he repeats his views and which shows that these remained unaltered from 1839 to 1857.

3. An Essay by Mr. Wallace, entitled "On the Tendency of Varieties to depart indefinitely from the Original Type." This was written at Ternate [2] in February 1858, for the perusal of his friend and correspondent Mr. Darwin, and sent to him with the expressed wish that it should be forwarded to Sir Charles Lyell, if Mr. Darwin thought it sufficiently novel and interesting. So highly did Mr. Darwin appreciate the value of the views therein set forth, that he proposed, in a letter to Sir Charles Lyell, to obtain Mr. Wallace's consent to allow the Essay to be published as soon as possible. Of this step we highly approved, provided Mr. Darwin did not withhold from the public, as he was strongly inclined to do (in favour of Mr. Wallace), the memoir which he had himself written on the same subject, and which, as before stated, one of us had perused in 1844, and the contents of which we had both of us been privy to for many years. On representing this to Mr. Darwin, he gave us permission to make what use we thought proper of his memoir, &c.; and in adopting our present course, of presenting it to the Linnean Society, we have explained to him that we are not solely considering the relative claims to priority of himself and his friend, but the interests of science generally; for we feel it to be desirable that views founded on a wide deduction from facts, and matured by years of reflection, should constitute at once a goal from which others may start, and that, while the scientific world is waiting for the appearance of Mr. Darwin's complete work, some of the leading results of his labours, as well as those of his able correspondent, should together be laid before the public.

We have the honour to be yours very obediently,

CHARLES LYELL.
JOS. D. HOOKER.

J. J. Bennett, Esq.,
Secretary of the Linnean Society.

∿

I—*Extract from an unpublished Work on Species, by* C. DARWIN, Esq. . . .

De Candolle,[3] in an eloquent passage, has declared that all nature

---

[2] Island in the Dutch East Indies.
[3] Augustin de Candolle (1778-1841), Swiss botanist

is at war, one organism with another, or with external nature.[46] Seeing the contented face of nature, this may at first well be doubted; but reflection will inevitably prove it to be true. The war, however, is not constant, but recurrent in a slight degree at short periods, and more severely at occasional more distant periods; and hence its effects are easily overlooked. It is the doctrine of Malthus applied in most cases with tenfold force.[4] As in every climate there are seasons, for each of its inhabitants, of greater and less abundance, so all annually breed; and the moral restraint which in some small degree checks the increase of mankind is entirely lost. Even slow-breeding mankind has doubled in twenty-five years; and if he could increase his food with greater ease, he would double in less time. But for animals without artificial means, the amount of food for each species must, *on an average*, be constant, whereas the increase of all organisms tends to be geometrical, and in a vast majority of cases at an enormous ratio. Suppose in a certain spot there are eight pairs of birds, and that *only* four pairs of them annually (including double hatches) rear only four young, and that these go on rearing their young at the same rate, then at the end of seven years (a short life, excluding violent deaths, for any bird) there will be 2048 birds, instead of the original sixteen. As this increase is quite impossible, we must conclude either that birds do not rear nearly half their young, or that the average life of a bird is, from accident, not nearly seven years. Both checks probably concur. The same kind of calculation applied to all plants and animals affords results more or less striking, but in very few instances more striking than in man.

Many practical illustrations of this rapid tendency to increase are on record, among which, during peculiar seasons, are the extraordinary numbers of certain animals; for instance, during the years 1826 to 1828, in La Plata,[5] when from drought some millions of cattle perished, the whole country *swarmed* with mice. Now I think it cannot be doubted that during the breeding-season all the mice (with the exception of a few males or females in excess) ordinarily pair, and therefore that this astounding increase during three years must be attributed to a greater number than usual surviving the first year, and then breeding, and so on till the third year, when their numbers were brought down to their usual limits on the return of wet weather. Where man has introduced plants and animals into a new and favourable country, there are many accounts in how surprisingly few years the whole country has become stocked with them. This increase would [47] necessarily stop as soon as the country was fully stocked; and yet we have every

---

[4] Thomas Malthus (1766-1834), English economist and sociologist, argued that population grows at a geometrical rate while the means of subsistence grows at a mere arithmetic rate. The result of this disparity is hunger and poverty unless war, famine, and disease intervene, or man exercises "moral restraint."

[5] Seaport in Argentina.

reason to believe, from what is known of wild animals, that *all* would pair in the spring. In the majority of cases it is most difficult to imagine where the checks fall—though generally, no doubt, on the seeds, eggs, and young; but when we remember how impossible, even in mankind (so much better known than any other animal), it is to infer from repeated casual observations what the average duration of life is, or to discover the different percentage of deaths to births in different countries, we ought to feel no surprise at our being unable to discover where the check falls in any animal or plant. It should always be remembered, that in most cases the checks are recurrent yearly in a small, regular degree, and in an extreme degree during unusually cold, hot, dry, or wet years, according to the constitution of the being in question. Lighten any check in the least degree, and the geometrical powers of increase in every organism will almost instantly increase the average number of the favoured species. Nature may be compared to a surface on which rest ten thousand sharp wedges touching each other and driven inwards by incessant blows. Fully to realize these views much reflection is requisite. Malthus on man should be studied; and all such cases as those of the mice in La Plata, of the cattle and horses when first turned out in South America, of the birds by our calculation, &c., should be well considered. Reflect on the enormous multiplying power *inherent and annually in action* in all animals; reflect on the countless seeds scattered by a hundred ingenious contrivances, year after year, over the whole face of the land; and yet we have every reason to suppose that the average percentage of each of the inhabitants of a country usually remains constant. Finally, let it be borne in mind that this average number of individuals (the external conditions remaining the same) in each country is kept up by recurrent struggles against other species or against external nature (as on the borders of the Arctic regions, where the cold checks life), and that ordinarily each individual of every species holds its place, either by its own struggle and capacity of acquiring nourishment in some period of its life, from the egg upwards; or by the struggle of its parents (in short-lived organisms, when the main check occurs at longer intervals) with other individuals of the *same* or *different* species.

But let the external conditions of a country alter. If in a small degree, the relative proportions of the inhabitants will in most cases simply be slightly changed; but let the number of [48] inhabitants be small, as on an island, and free access to it from other countries be circumscribed, and let the change of conditions continue progressing (forming new stations), in such a case the original inhabitants must cease to be as perfectly adapted to the changed conditions as they were originally. It has been shown in a former part of this work, that such changes of external conditions would, from their acting on the reproductive system, probably cause the organization of those beings which were most affected to become, as under domestication, plastic. Now, can it be doubted, from the struggle each individual has to obtain subsistence, that any minute variation in structure, habits, or instincts, adapting that individual better to the new conditions, would tell upon its vigour and health? In the struggle it would have a better *chance* of surviving; and those of its offspring which inherited the variation, be it ever so slight, would also have a better *chance*. Yearly more are bred than can survive; the smallest grain in the balance, in the long run, must tell on which death shall fall, and which shall survive. Let this work of selection on the one hand, and death on the other, go on for a thousand generations, who will pretend to affirm that it would produce no effect, when we remember what, in a few years, Bakewell [6] effected in cattle, and Western [7] in sheep, by this identical principle of selection?

To give an imaginary example from changes in progress on an is-land:—let the organization of a canine animal which preyed chiefly on rabbits, but sometimes on hares, become slightly plastic; let these same changes cause the number of rabbits very slowly to decrease, and the number of hares to increase; the effect of this would be that the fox or dog would be driven to try to catch more hares: his organization, however, being slightly plastic, those individuals with the lightest forms, longest limbs, and best eyesight, let the difference be ever so small, would be slightly favoured, and would tend to live longer, and to survive during that time of the year when food was scarcest; they would also rear more young, which would tend to inherit these slight peculiarities. The less fleet ones would be rigidly destroyed. I can see no more reason to doubt that these causes in a thousand generations would produce a marked effect, and adapt the form of the fox or dog to the catching of hares instead of rabbits, than that greyhounds can be improved by selection and careful breeding. So would it be with plants under similar circumstances. If the number of individuals of a species with plumed seeds could be increased by greater powers of dissemination within its own area [49] (that is, if the check to increase fell chiefly on the seeds), those seeds which were provided with ever so little more down, would in the long run be most disseminated; hence a greater number of seeds thus formed would germinate; and would tend to produce plants inheriting the slightly better-adapted down. [8]

Besides this natural means of selection, by which those individuals are preserved, whether in their egg, or larval, or mature state, which are best adapted to the place they fill in nature, there is a second agency at work in most unisexual animals, tending to produce the same effect, namely, the struggle of the males for the females. These struggles are

---

[6] Robert Bakewell (1725-1795), English agriculturalist.

[7] Charles Western (1767-1844), English political figure and experimental sheep breeder.

[8] I can see no more difficulty in this, than in the planter improving his varieties of the cotton plant. [Darwin's note in 1858.]

generally decided by the law of battle, but in the case of birds, apparently, by the charms of their song, by their beauty or their power of courtship, as in the dancing rock-thrush of Guiana. The most vigorous and healthy males, implying perfect adaptation, must generally gain the victory in their contests. This kind of selection, however, is less rigorous than the other; it does not require the death of the less successful, but gives to them fewer descendants. The struggle falls, moreover, at a time of year when food is generally abundant, and perhaps the effect chiefly produced would be the modification of the secondary sexual characters, which are not related to the power of obtaining food, or to defence from animals, but to fighting with or rivalling other males. The result of this struggle amongst the males may be compared in some respects to that produced by those agriculturalists who pay less attention to the careful selection of all their young animals, and more to the occasional use of a choice mate.

II—*Abstract of a Letter from* C. DARWIN, Esq., *to* Prof. ASA GRAY, *Boston, U.S., dated Down,*[9] *September 5th, 1857.*

1. It is wonderful what the principle of selection by man, that is the picking out of individuals with any desired quality, and breeding from them, and again picking out, can do. Even breeders have been astounded at their own results. They can act on differences inappreciable to an uneducated eye. Selection has been *methodically* followed in *Europe* for only the last half century; but it was occasionally, and even in some degree methodically, followed in the most ancient times. There must have been also a kind of unconscious selection from a remote period, namely in [50] the preservation of the individual animals (without any thought of their offspring) most useful to each race of man in his particular circumstances. The "roguing," as nurserymen call the destroying of varieties which depart from their type, is a kind of selection. I am convinced that intentional and occasional selection has been the main agent in the production of our domestic races; but however this may be, its great power of modification has been indisputably shown in later times. Selection acts only by the accumulation of slight or greater variations, caused by external conditions, or by the mere fact that in generation the child is not absolutely similar to its parent. Man, by this power of accumulating variations, adapts living beings to his wants—may be said to make the wool of one sheep good for carpets, of another for cloth, &c.

2. Now suppose there were a being who did not judge by mere external appearances, but who could study the whole internal organization, who was never capricious, and should go on selecting for

---

[9] Down House, Darwin's country estate in Kent, not far from London.

one object during millions of generations; who will say what he might not effect? In nature we have some *slight* variation occasionally in all parts; and I think it can be shown that changed conditions of existence is [*sic*] the main cause of the child not exactly resembling its parents; and in nature geology shows us what changes have taken place, and are taking place. We have almost unlimited time; no one but a practical geologist can fully appreciate this. Think of the Glacial period, during the whole of which the same species at least of shells have existed; there must have been during this period millions on millions of generations.

3. I think it can be shown that there is such an unerring power at work in *Natural Selection* (the title of my book),[10] which selects exclusively for the good of each organic being. The elder De Candolle, W. Herbert,[11] and Lyell have written excellently on the struggle for life; but even they have not written strongly enough. Reflect that every being (even the elephant) breeds at such a rate, that in a few years, or at most a few centuries, the surface of the earth would not hold the progeny of one pair. I have found it hard constantly to bear in mind that the increase of every single species is checked during some part of its life, or during some shortly recurrent generation. Only a few of those annually born can live to propagate their kind. What a trifling difference must often determine which shall survive, and which perish!

4. Now take the case of a country undergoing some change. This will tend to cause some of its inhabitants to vary slightly—[51] not but that I believe most beings vary at all times enough for selection to act on them. Some of its inhabitants will be exterminated; and the remainder will be exposed to the mutual action of a different set of inhabitants, which I believe to be far more important to the life of each being than mere climate. Considering the infinitely various methods which living beings follow to obtain food by struggling with other organisms, to escape danger at various times of life, to have their eggs or seeds disseminated, &c. &c., I cannot doubt that during millions of generations individuals of a species will be occasionally born with some slight variation, profitable to some part of their economy. Such individuals will have a better chance of surviving, and of propagating their new and slightly different structure; and the modification may be slowly increased by the accumulative action of natural selection to any profitable extent. The variety thus formed will either coexist with, or, more commonly, will exterminate its parent form. An organic being, like the woodpecker or misseltoe [*sic*], may thus come to be adapted to a score of contingences—natural selection ac-

---

10 That is, the book that turned out to be *The Origin of Species*.
11 William Herbert, Dean of Manchester (1778-1847), classical scholar and naturalist.

cumulating those slight variations in all parts of its structure, which are in any way useful to it during any part of its life.

5. Multiform difficulties will occur to every one, with respect to this theory. Many can, I think, be satisfactorily answered. *Natura non facit saltum* [12] answers some of the most obvious. The slowness of the change, and only a very few individuals undergoing change at any one time, answers others. The extreme imperfection of our geological records answers others.

6. Another principle, which may be called the principle of divergence, plays, I believe, an important part in the origin of species. The same spot will support more life if occupied by very diverse forms. We see this in the many generic forms in a square yard of turf, and in the plants or insects on any little uniform islet, belonging almost invariably to as many genera and families as species. We can understand the meaning of this fact amongst the higher animals, whose habits we understand. We know that it has been experimentally shown that a plot of land will yield a greater weight if sown with several species and genera of grasses, than if sown with only two or three species. Now, every organic being, by propagating so rapidly, may be said to be striving its utmost to increase in numbers. So it will be with the offspring of any species after it has become diversified into varieties, or subspecies, or true species. And it follows, I think, from the foregoing facts, that the varying offspring of each species will try [52] (only few will succeed) to seize on as many and as diverse places in the economy of nature as possible. Each new variety or species, when formed, will generally take the place of, and thus exterminate its less well-fitted parent. This I believe to be the origin of the classification and affinities of organic beings at all times; for organic beings always *seem* to branch and sub-branch like the limbs of a tree from a common trunk, the flourishing and diverging twigs destroying the less vigorous—the dead and lost branches rudely representing extinct genera and families.

This sketch is *most* imperfect; but in so short a space I cannot make it better. Your imagination must fill up very wide blanks.

C. DARWIN.

III—*On the Tendency of Varieties to depart indefinitely from the Original Type*. By ALFRED RUSSEL WALLACE.

One of the strongest arguments which have been adduced to prove the original and permanent distinctness of species is, that *varieties* produced in a state of domesticity are more or less unstable, and

---

[12] Nature makes no jump (i.e., changes in nature are slow and constant rather than sudden and periodic).

often have a tendency, if left to themselves, to return to the normal form of the parent species; and this instability is considered to be a distinctive peculiarity of all varieties, even of those occurring among wild animals in a state of nature, and to constitute a provision for preserving unchanged the originally created distinct species.

In the absence or scarcity of facts and observations as to *varieties* occurring among wild animals, this argument has had great weight with naturalists, and has led to a very general and somewhat prejudiced belief in the stability of species. Equally general, however, is the belief in what are called "permanent or true varieties,"—races of animals which continually propagate their like, but which differ so slightly (although constantly) from some other race, that the one is considered to be a *variety* of the other. Which is the *variety* and which the original *species*, there is generally no means of determining, except in those rare cases in which the one race has been known to produce an offspring unlike itself and resembling the other. This, however, would seem quite incompatible with the "permanent invariability of species," but the difficulty is overcome by assuming that such varieties have strict limits, and can never again vary further from the original type, although they may return to it, which, from the [53] analogy of the domesticated animals, is considered to be highly probable, if not certainly proved.

It will be observed that this argument rests entirely on the assumption, that *varieties* occurring in a state of nature are in all respects analogous to or even identical with those of domestic animals, and are governed by the same laws as regards their permanence or further variation. But it is the object of the present paper to show that this assumption is altogether false, that there is a general principle in nature which will cause many varieties to survive the parent species, and to give rise to successive variations departing further and further from the original type, and which also produces, in domesticated animals, the tendency of varieties to return to the parent form.

The life of wild animals is a struggle for existence. The full exertion of all their faculties and all their energies is required to preserve their own existence and provide for that of their infant offspring. The possibility of procuring food during the least favourable seasons, and of escaping the attacks of their most dangerous enemies, are the primary conditions which determine the existence both of individuals and of entire species. These conditions will also determine the population of a species; and by a careful consideration of all the circumstances we may be enabled to comprehend, and in some degree to explain, what at first sight appears so inexplicable—the excessive abundance of some species, while others closely allied to them are very rare. . . . [54] . . . .

Now it is clear that what takes place among the individuals of a species must also occur among the several allied species of a group,—

viz. that those which are best adapted to obtain a regular supply of food, and to defend themselves against the attacks of their enemies and the vicissitudes of the seasons, must necessarily obtain and preserve a superiority in population; while those species which from some defect of power or organization are the least capable of counteracting the vicissitudes of food, supply, &c., must diminish in numbers, and, in extreme cases, become altogether extinct. Between these extremes the species will present various degrees of capacity for ensuring the means of preserving life; and it is thus we account for the abundance or rarity of species. Our ignorance will generally prevent us from accurately tracing the effects to their causes; but could we become perfectly acquainted with the organization and habits of the various species of animals, and could we measure the capacity of each for performing the different acts necessary to its safety and existence under all the varying circumstances by which it is surrounded, we might be able even to calculate the proportionate abundance of individuals which is the necessary result.

If now we have succeeded in establishing these two points—1st, *that the animal population of a country is generally stationary, being kept down by a periodical deficiency of food, and other checks;* and, 2nd, *that the comparative abundance or scarcity of the individuals of the several species is entirely due to their organization and resulting habits, which, rendering it more difficult to procure a regular supply of food and to provide for their personal safety in some cases than in others, can only be balanced by a difference in the population which have to exist in a given area*—we shall be in a condition to proceed to the consideration of *varieties,* to which the preceding remarks have a direct and very important application.

Most or perhaps all the variations from the typical form of a species must have some definite effect, however slight, on the habits or capacities of the individuals. Even a change of colour might, by rendering them more or less distinguishable, affect their safety; a greater or less development of hair might modify their habits. More important changes, such as an increase in the power or dimensions of the limbs or any of the external organs, would more or less affect their mode of procuring food or the range of [57] country which they inhabit. It is also evident that most changes would affect, either favourably or adversely, the powers of prolonging existence. An antelope with shorter or weaker legs must necessarily suffer more from the attacks of the feline carnivora; the passenger pigeon with less powerful wings would sooner or later be affected in its powers of procuring a regular supply of food; and in both cases the result must necessarily be a diminution of the population of the modified species. If, on the other hand, any species should produce a variety having slightly increased powers of preserving existence, that variety must inevitably in time acquire a superiority in numbers. These results must follow as surely as old age, intemperance, or scarcity of food produce an in-creased mortality. In both cases there may be many individual ex-ceptions; but on the average the rule will invariably be found to hold good. All varieties will therefore fall into two classes—those which under the same conditions would never reach the population of the parent species, and those which would in time obtain and keep a numerical superiority. Now, let some alteration of physical conditions occur in the district—a long period of drought, a destruction of vegeta-tion by locusts, the irruption of some new carnivorous animal seeking "pastures new"—any change in fact tending to render existence more difficult to the species in question, and tasking its utmost powers to avoid complete extermination; it is evident that, of all the individuals composing the species, those forming the least numerous and most feebly organized variety would suffer first, and, were the pressure severe, must soon become extinct. The same causes continuing in action, the parent species would next suffer, would gradually diminish in numbers, and with a recurrence of similar unfavourable conditions might also become extinct. The superior variety would then alone remain, and on a return to favourable circumstances would rapidly increase in numbers and occupy the place of the extinct species and variety.

The *variety* would now have replaced the *species*, of which it would be a more perfectly developed and more highly organized form. It would be in all respects better adapted to secure its safety, and to prolong its individual existence and that of the race. Such a variety *could not* return to the original form; for that form is an inferior one, and could never compete with it for existence. Granted, therefore, a "tendency" to reproduce the original type of the species, still the variety must ever remain preponderant in numbers, and under adverse physical conditions *again alone survive*.[58] But this new, improved, and populous race might itself, in course of time, give rise to new varieties, exhibiting several diverging modifications of form, any of which, tending to increase the facilities for preserving existence, must, by the same general law, in their turn become pre-dominant. Here, then, we have *progression and continued divergence* deduced from the general laws which regulate the existence of ani-mals in a state of nature, and from the undisputed fact that varieties do frequently occur. It is not, however, contended that this re-sult would be invariable; a change of physical conditions in the dis-trict might at times materially modify it, rendering the race which had been the most capable of supporting existence under the former con-ditions now the least so, and even causing the extinction of the newer and, for a time, superior race, while the old or parent species and its first inferior varieties continued to flourish. . . . The scale on which nature works is so vast—the numbers of individuals and periods of time with which she deals approach so near to infinity, that any cause, however slight, and however liable to be veiled and counteracted by accidental circumstances, must in the end produce its full legitimate results.

Let us now turn to domesticated animals, and inquire how varieties produced among them are affected by the principles here enunciated. The essential difference in the condition of wild and domestic animals is this,—that among the former, their well-being and very existence depend upon the full exercise and healthy condition of all their senses and physical powers, whereas, among the latter, these are only partially exercised, and in some cases are absolutely unused. A wild animal has to search, and often to labour, for every mouthful of food—to exercise sight, hearing, and smell in seeking it, and in avoiding dangers, in procuring shelter from the inclemency of the seasons, and in providing the subsistence and safety of its offspring. There is no muscle of [59] its body that is not called into daily and hourly activity; there is no sense or faculty that is not strengthened by continual exercise. The domestic animal, on the other hand, has food provided for it, is sheltered, and often confined, to guard it against the vicissitudes of the seasons, is carefully secured from the attacks of its natural enemies, and seldom even rears its young without human assistance. Half of its senses and faculties are quite useless; and the other half are but occasionally called into feeble exercise, while even its muscular system is only irregularly called into action.

Now when a variety of such an animal occurs, having increased power or capacity in any organ or sense, such increase is totally useless, is never called into action, and may even exist without the animal ever becoming aware of it. In the wild animal, on the contrary, all its faculties and powers being brought into full action for the necessities of existence, any increase becomes immediately available, is strengthened by exercise, and must even slightly modify the food, the habits, and the whole economy of the race. It creates as it were a new animal, one of superior powers, and which will necessarily increase in numbers and outlive those inferior to it.

Again, in the domesticated animal all variations have an equal chance of continuance; and those which would decidedly render a wild animal unable to compete with its fellows and continue its existence are no disadvantage whatever in a state of domesticity. . . .[60]

We see, then, that no inferences as to varieties in a state of nature can be deduced from the observation of those occurring among domestic animals. The two are so much opposed to each other in every circumstance of their existence, that what applies to the one is almost sure not to apply to the other. . . .

The hypothesis of Lamarck [13]—that progressive changes in species

---

[13] Jean Baptiste Pierre Antoine de Monet, Chevalier de Lamarck (1744-1829), French naturalist and one of Darwin's and Wallace's most distinguished predecessors as a theorizer on evolution. See Introduction.

have been produced by the attempts of animals to increase the development of their own organs, and thus modify their structure and habits—has been repeatedly and easily refuted by all writers on the subject of varieties and species . . . ; but the view here developed renders such an hypothesis quite unnecessary, by showing that similar results must be produced by the action of principles constantly at work in nature. The powerful retractile talons of the falcon- and the cat-tribes have not been produced or increased by the volition of those animals; but among the different varieties which occurred in the earlier and less highly organized forms of these groups, *those always survived longest which had the greatest facilities for seizing their prey*. . . .[61]. . . .

We believe we have now shown that there is a tendency in nature to the continued progression of certain classes of *varieties* further and further from the original type—a progression to which there appears no reason to assign any definite limits—and that the same principle which produces this result in a state of nature will also explain why domestic varieties have a tendency to revert to the original type. This progression, by minute steps, in various directions, but always checked and balanced by the necessary conditions, subject to which alone existence can be preserved, may, it is believed, be followed out so as to agree with all the phenomena presented by organized beings, their extinction and succession in past ages, and all the extraordinary modifications of form, instinct, and habits which they exhibit.

Ternate, February, 1858.[62]

Charles Darwin (1809-1882)

From *On the Origin of Species by Means of Natural Selection, or the Preservation of Favoured Races in the Struggle for Life*. 6th ed. London: John Murray, 1878. (Published originally in 1859.)

INTRODUCTION:

When on board H.M.S. 'Beagle,' as naturalist, I was much struck with certain facts in the distribution of the organic beings inhabiting South America, and in the geological relations of the present to the past inhabitants of that continent. These facts, as will be seen in the latter chapters of this volume, seemed to throw some light on the origin of species—that mystery of mysteries, as it has been called by one of our greatest philosophers. On my return home, it occurred to me, in 1837, that something might perhaps be made out on this question by patiently accumulating and reflecting on all sorts of facts which could possibly have any bearing on it. After five years' work I allowed myself to speculate on the subject, and drew up some short notes; these I enlarged in 1844 into a sketch of the conclusions, which then seemed to me probable: from that period to the present day I have steadily pursued the same object. I hope that I may be excused for entering on these personal details, as I give them to show that I have not been hasty in coming to a decision.

My work is now (1859) nearly finished; but as it will take me many more years to complete it, and as my health is far from strong, I have been urged to publish this Abstract. I have more especially been induced to do this, as Mr. Wallace, who is now studying the natural history of the Malay archipelago, has arrived at almost exactly the same general conclusions that I have on the origin of species. In 1858 he sent me a memoir on this subject, with a request that I would forward it to Sir Charles Lyell, who sent it to the Linnean Society, and it is published in the third volume of the Journal of that society. Sir C. Lyell and Dr. Hooker, who both knew of my work—the latter having read my sketch of 1844—honoured me by thinking it advisable to publish, with Mr. Wallace's excellent memoir, some brief extracts from my manuscripts. . . .[1] . . . .

In considering the Origin of Species, it is quite conceivable that a naturalist, reflecting on the mutual affinities of organic beings, on their embryological relations, their geographical distribution, geological succession, and other such facts, might come to the conclusion that species had not been independently created, but had descended, like varieties, from other species. Nevertheless, such a conclusion, even if well founded, would be unsatisfactory, until it could be shown how the innumerable species inhabiting this world have been modified, so as to acquire that perfection of structure and coadaptation which justly excites our admiration. Naturalists continually refer to external conditions, such as climate, food, &c., as the only possible cause of variation. In one limited sense, as we shall hereafter see, this may be true; but it is preposterous to attribute to mere external conditions, the structure, for instance, of the woodpecker, with its feet, tail, beak, and tongue, so admirably adapted to catch insects under the bark of trees. In the case of the mistletoe, which draws its nourishment from certain trees, which has seeds that must be transported by certain birds, and which has flowers with separate sexes absolutely requiring the agency of certain insects to bring pollen from one flower to the other, it is equally preposterous to account for the structure of this parasite, with its relations to several distinct organic beings, by the effects [2] of external conditions, or of habit, or of the volition of the plant itself.

It is, therefore, of the highest importance to gain a clear insight into the means of modification and coadaptation. At the commencement of my observations it seemed to me probable that a careful study of domesticated animals and of cultivated plants would offer the best chance of making out this obscure problem. Nor have I been disappointed; in this and in all other perplexing cases I have invariably found that our knowledge, imperfect though it be, of variation under domestication, afforded the best and safest clue. I may venture to express my conviction of the high value of such studies, although they have been very commonly neglected by naturalists.

From these considerations, I shall devote the first chapter of this Abstract to Variation under Domestication. We shall thus see that a large amount of hereditary modification is at least possible; and what is equally or more important, we shall see how great is the power of man in accumulating by his Selection successive slight variations. I will then pass on to the variability of species in a state of nature; but I shall, unfortunately, be compelled to treat this subject far too briefly, as it can be treated properly only by giving long catalogues of facts. We shall, however, be enabled to discuss what circumstances are most favourable to variation. In the next chapter the Struggle for Existence amongst all organic beings throughout the world, which inevitably follows from the high geometrical ratio of their increase, will be considered. This is the doctrine of Malthus, applied to the whole animal and vegetable kingdoms. As many more individuals of each species are born than can possibly survive; and as, consequently, there is a frequently recurring struggle for existence, it follows that any being, if it vary however slightly in any manner profitable to itself, under the complex and sometimes varying conditions of life, will have a better chance of surviving, and thus be *naturally selected.* From the strong principle of inheritance, any selected variety will tend to propagate its new and modified form.

This fundamental subject of Natural Selection will be treated at some length in the fourth chapter; and we shall then see how Natural Selection almost inevitably causes much Extinction of the less improved forms of life, and leads to what I have called Divergence of Character. In the next chapter I shall discuss the complex and little known laws of variation. In the five succeeding chapters, the most apparent and gravest difficulties in accepting the theory will be given: namely, first, the difficulties of transitions, or how a [3] simple being or a simple organ can be changed and perfected into a highly developed being or into an elaborately constructed organ; secondly, the subject of Instinct, or the mental powers of animals; thirdly, Hybridism, or the infertility of species and the fertility of varieties when intercrossed; and fourthly, the imperfection of the Geological Record. In the next chapter I shall consider the geological succession of organic beings throughout time; in the twelfth and thirteenth, their geographical distribution throughout space; in the fourteenth, their classification or mutual affinities, both when mature and in an embryonic condition. In the last chapter I shall give a brief recapitulation of the whole work and a few concluding remarks.

No one ought to feel surprise at much remaining as yet unexplained in regard to the origin of species and varieties, if he make due allowance for our profound ignorance in regard to the mutual relations of the many beings which live around us. Who can explain why one species ranges widely and is very numerous, and why another allied species has a narrow range and is rare? Yet these relations are of the highest importance, for they determine the present welfare and, as I believe, the future success and modification of every inhabitant of this world. Still less do we know of the mutual relations of the innumerable inhabitants of the world during the many past geological epochs in its history. Although much remains obscure, and will long remain obscure, I can entertain no doubt, after the most deliberate study and dispassionate judgment of which I am capable, that the view which most naturalists until recently entertained, and which I formerly entertained—namely, that each species has been independently created—is erroneous. I am fully convinced that species are not immutable; but that those belonging to what are called the same genera are lineal descendants of some other and generally extinct species, in the same manner as the acknowledged varieties of any one species are the descendants of that species. Furthermore, I am convinced that Natural Selection has been the most important, but not the exclusive, means of modification.[4]

CHAPTER XV—"RECAPITULATION AND CONCLUSION"

I have now recapitulated the facts and considerations which have thoroughly convinced me that species have been modified, during a long course of descent. This has been effected chiefly through the natural selection of numerous successive, slight, favourable variations; aided in an important manner by the inherited effects of the use and disuse of parts; and in an unimportant manner, that is in relation to adaptive structures, whether past or present, by the direct action of external conditions, and by variations which seem to us in our ignorance to arise spontaneously. It appears that I formerly underrated the frequency and value of these latter forms of variation, as leading to permanent modifications of structure independently of natural selection. But as my conclusions have lately been much misrepresented, and it has been stated that I attribute the modification of species exclusively to natural selection, I may be permitted to remark that in the first edition of this work, and subsequently, I placed in a most conspicuous position—namely, at the close of the Introduction—the following words: "I am convinced that natural selection has been the main but not the exclusive means of modification." This has been of no avail. Great is the power of steady misrepresentation; but the history of science shows that fortunately this power does not long endure. . . .

I see no good reason why the views given in this volume should shock the religious feelings of any one. It is satisfactory, as showing how transient such impressions are, to remember that the greatest discovery ever made by man, namely, the law of the [421] attraction of gravity, was also attacked by Leibnitz,[1] "as subversive of natural, and inferentially of revealed, religion." A celebrated author and divine has written to me that "he has gradually learnt to see that it is just as noble a conception of the Deity to believe that He created a few original forms capable of self-development into other and needful forms, as to believe that He required a fresh act of creation to supply the voids caused by the action of His laws."

Why, it may be asked, until recently did nearly all the most eminent living naturalists and geologists disbelieve in the mutability of species? It cannot be asserted that organic beings in a state of nature are subject to no variation; it cannot be proved that the amount of variation in the course of long ages is a limited quality; no clear distinction has been, or can be, drawn between species and well-marked varieties. It cannot be maintained that species when intercrossed are invariably sterile, and varieties invariably fertile; or that sterility is a special endowment and sign of creation.[2] The belief that species were immutable productions was almost unavoidable as long as the history of the world was thought to be of short duration; and now that we have acquired some idea of the lapse of time, we are too apt to assume, without proof, that the geological record is so perfect that it would have afforded us plain evidence of the mutation of species, if they had undergone mutation.

But the chief cause of our natural unwillingness to admit that one species has given birth to other and distinct species, is that we are always slow in admitting great changes of which we do not see the steps. The difficulty is the same as that felt by so many geologists, when Lyell first insisted that long lines of inland cliffs had been formed, and great valleys excavated, by the agencies which we see still at work. The mind cannot possibly grasp the full meaning of the term of even a million years; it cannot add up and perceive the full effects of many slight variations, accumulated during an almost infinite number of generations.

Although I am fully convinced of the truth of the views given in this volume under the form of an abstract, I by no means expect to convince experienced naturalists whose minds are stocked with a mul-

---

[1] Baron Gottfried Wilhelm von Leibnitz (1646-1716), German mathematician and philosopher.

[2] A belief widely held among biologists has been that individuals of different species will usually not breed with one another, and that if they do, their progeny will be sterile. See pp. 43, 47-48, 75, 80, 82.

titude of facts all viewed, during a long course of years, from a point of view directly opposite to mine. It is so easy to hide our ignorance under such expressions as the "plan of creation," "unity of design," &c., and to think that we give an explanation when we only re-state a fact. Any one whose disposition leads him to attach more weight to unexplained difficulties than to the explanation of [422] a certain number of facts will certainly reject the theory. A few naturalists, endowed with much flexibility of mind, may be influenced by this volume; but I look with confidence to the future,—to young and rising naturalists, who will be able to view both sides of the question with impartiality. Whoever is led to believe that species are mutable will do good service by conscientiously expressing his conviction; for thus only can the load of prejudice by which this subject is overwhelmed be removed.

Several eminent naturalists have of late published their belief that a multitude of reputed species in each genus are not real species; but that other species are real, that is, have been independently created. This seems to me a strange conclusion to arrive at. They admit that a multitude of forms, which till lately they themselves thought were special creations, and which are still thus looked at by the majority of naturalists, and which consequently have all the external characteristic features of true species,—they admit that these have been produced by variation, but they refuse to extend the same view to other and slightly different forms. Nevertheless they do not pretend that they can define, or even conjecture, which are the created forms of life, and which are those produced by secondary laws. They admit variation as a *vera causa* [3] in one case, they arbitrarily reject it in another, without assigning any distinction in the two cases. The day will come when this will be given as a curious illustration of the blindness of preconceived opinion. These authors seem no more startled at a miraculous act of creation than at an ordinary birth. But do they really believe that at innumerable periods in the earth's history certain elemental atoms have been commanded suddenly to flash into living tissues? Do they believe that at each supposed act of creation one individual or many were produced? Were all the infinitely numerous kinds of animals and plants created as eggs or seed, or as full grown? and in the case of mammals, were they created bearing the false marks of nourishment from the mother's womb? . . . . [423]

As a record of a former state of things, I have retained in the foregoing paragraphs, and elsewhere, several sentences which imply that naturalists believe in the separate creation of each species; and I have been much censured for having thus expressed myself. But undoubtedly this was the general belief when the first edition of the present work appeared. I formerly spoke to very many naturalists on the subject of evolution, and never once met with any sympathetic agreement. It is

---

[3] True cause.

probable that some did then believe in evolution, but they were either silent, or expressed themselves so ambiguously that it was not easy to understand their meaning. Now things are wholly changed, and almost every naturalist admits the great principle of evolution. There are, however, some who still think that species have suddenly given birth, through quite unexplained means, to new and totally different forms: but, as I have attempted to show, weighty evidence can be opposed to the admission of great and abrupt modifications. Under a scientific point of view, and as leading to further investigation, but little advantage is gained by believing that new forms are suddenly developed in an inexplicable manner from old and widely different forms, over the old belief in the creation of species from the dust of the earth. . . .

Organs in a rudimentary condition plainly show that an early progenitor had the organ in a fully developed condition; and this in some cases implies an enormous amount of modification in the descendants. Throughout whole classes various structures are formed on the same pattern, and at a very early age the embryos closely resemble each other. Therefore I cannot doubt that the theory of descent with modification embraces all the members of the same great class or kingdom. I believe that animals are descended from at most only four or five progenitors, and plants from an equal or lesser number.

Analogy would lead me one step farther, namely, to the belief that all animals and plants are descended from some one prototype. But analogy may be a deceitful guide. Nevertheless all living [424] things have much in common, in their chemical composition, their cellular structure, their laws of growth, and their liability to injurious influences. We see this even in so trifling a fact as that the same poison often similarly affects plants and animals; or that the poison secreted by the gall-fly produces monstrous growths on the wild rose or oak-tree. With all organic beings excepting perhaps some of the very lowest, sexual production seems to be essentially similar. With all, as far as is at present known, the germinal vesicle is the same; so that all organisms start from a common origin. . . . On the principle of natural selection with divergence of character, it does not seem incredible that, from such low and intermediate form, both animals and plants may have been developed; and, if we admit this, we must likewise admit that all the organic beings which have ever lived on this earth may be descended from some one primordial form. . . .[425] . . .

Authors of the highest eminence seem to be fully satisfied with the view that each species has been independently created. To my mind it accords better with what we know of the laws impressed on matter by the Creator, that the production and extinction of the past and present inhabitants of the world should have been due to secondary causes, like those determining the birth and death of the individual. When I view all beings not as special creations, but as the lineal descendants of some few beings which lived long before the first bed of the Cambrian [4] system was deposited, they seem to me to become ennobled. . . . As all the living forms of life are the lineal descendants of those which lived long before the Cambrian epoch, we may feel certain that the ordinary succession by generation has never once been broken, and that no cataclysm has desolated the whole world. Hence we may look with some confidence to a secure future of great length. And as natural selection works solely by and for the good of each being, all corporeal and mental endowments will tend to progress towards perfection.[428]

It is interesting to contemplate a tangled bank, clothed with many plants of many kinds, with birds singing on the bushes, with various insects flitting about, and with worms crawling through the damp earth, and to reflect that these elaborately constructed forms, so different from each other, and dependent upon each other in so complex a manner, have all been produced by laws acting around us. These laws, taken in the largest sense, being Growth with Reproduction; Inheritance which is almost implied by reproduction; Variability from the indirect and direct action of the conditions of life, and from use and disuse: a Ratio of Increase so high as to lead to a Struggle for Life, and as a consequence to Natural Selection, entailing Divergence of Character and the Extinction of less-improved forms. Thus, from the war of nature, from famine and death, the most exalted object which we are capable of conceiving, namely the production of the higher animals, directly follows. There is grandeur in this view of life, with its several powers, having been originally breathed by the Creator into a few forms or into one; and that, whilst this planet has gone cycling on according to the fixed law of gravity, from so simple a beginning endless forms most beautiful and most wonderful have been, and are being evolved.[429]

~

From *The Descent of Man, and Selection in Relation to Sex.* 2nd ed. London: John Murray, 1874. (Published originally in 1871.)

INTRODUCTION:

The nature of the following work will be best understood by a brief account of how it came to be written. During many years I collected notes on the origin or descent of man, without any intention of publishing on the subject, but rather with the determination not to publish, as I thought that I should thus only add to the prejudices against my views. It seemed to me sufficient to indicate, in the first

----

[4] Earliest period of the Paleozoic era of geological time. See Glossary.

edition of my 'Origin of Species,' that by this work "light would be thrown on the origin of man and his history;" and this implies that man must be included with other organic beings in any general conclusion respecting his manner of appearance on this earth. Now the case wears a wholly different aspect. . . . It is manifest that at least a large number of naturalists must admit that species are the modified descendants of other species; and this especially holds good with the younger and rising naturalists. The greater number accept the agency of natural selection; though some urge, whether with justice the future must decide, that I have greatly overrated its importance. Of the older and honoured chiefs in natural science, many unfortunately are still opposed to evolution in every form.

In consequence of the views now adopted by most naturalists, and which will ultimately, as in every other case, be followed by [1] others who are not scientific, I have been led to put together my notes, so as to see how far the general conclusions arrived at in my former works were applicable to man. . . .

The sole object of this work is to consider, firstly, whether man, like every other species, is descended from some pre-existing form; secondly, the manner of his development; and thirdly, the value of the differences between the so-called races of man. As I shall confine myself to these points, it will not be necessary to describe in detail the differences between the several races—an enormous subject which has been fully discussed in many valuable works. The high antiquity of man has recently been demonstrated by the labours of a host of eminent men, beginning with M. Boucher de Perthes;[1] and this is the indispensable basis for understanding his origin. I shall, therefore, take this conclusion for granted, and may refer my readers to the admirable treatises of Sir Charles Lyell, Sir John Lubbock,[2] and others. Nor shall I have occasion to do more than to allude to the amount of difference between man and the anthropomorphous apes; for Prof. Huxley, in the opinion of most competent judges, has conclusively shewn that in every visible character man differs less from the higher apes, than these do from the lower members of the same order of Primates. . . .[2] . . . .

During many years it has seemed to me highly probable that sexual selection has played an important part in differentiating the races of man; but in my 'Origin of Species' (first edition, p. 199) I contented myself by merely alluding to this belief. When I came to apply this view to man, I found it indispensable to treat the whole subject in full detail. Consequently the second part of the present work, treating of sexual selection, has extended to an inordinate length, compared with the first part; but this could not be avoided. . . .[3]

---

[1] Jacques Boucher de Crèvecoeur de Perthes (1788-1868), French writer and archaeologist.

[2] Sir John Lubbock (1834-1913), English naturalist.

CHAPTER XXI—"GENERAL SUMMARY AND CONCLUSION"

The main conclusion here arrived at, and now held by many naturalists who are well competent to form a sound judgment is that man is descended from some less highly organised form. The grounds upon which this conclusion rests will never be shaken, for the close similarity between man and the lower animals in embryonic development, as well as in innumerable points of structure and constitution, both of high and of the most trifling importance,—the rudiments which he retains, and the abnormal reversions to which he is occasionally liable,—[606] are facts which cannot be disputed. They have long been known, but until recently they told us nothing with respect to the origin of man. Now when viewed by the light of our knowledge of the whole organic world, their meaning is unmistakable. The great principle of evolution stands up clear and firm, when these groups of facts are considered in connection with others, such as the mutual affinities of the members of the same group, their geographical distribution in past and present times, and their geological succession. It is incredible that all these facts should speak falsely. He who is not content to look, like a savage, at the phenomena of nature as disconnected, cannot any longer believe that man is the work of a separate act of creation. He will be forced to admit that the close resemblance of the embryo of man to that, for instance, of a dog—the construction of his skull, limbs and whole frame on the same plan with that of other mammals, independently of the uses to which the parts may be put—the occasional re-appearance of various structures, for instance of several muscles, which man does not normally possess, but which are common to the Quadrumana [3]—and a crowd of analogous facts—all point in the plainest manner to the conclusion that man is the co-descendant with other mammals of a common progenitor.

We have seen that man incessantly presents individual differences in all parts of his body and in his mental faculties. These differences or variations seem to be induced by the same general causes, and to obey the same laws as with the lower animals. In both cases similar laws of inheritance prevail. Man tends to increase at a greater rate than his means of subsistence; consequently he is occasionally subjected to a severe struggle for existence, and natural selection will have effected whatever lies within its scope. A succession of strongly-marked variations of a similar nature is by no means requisite; slight fluctuating differences in the individual suffice for the work of natural selection; not that we have any reason to suppose that in the same species, all parts of the organisation tend to vary to the same degree. We may feel assured that the inherited effects of the long-continued use or

---

[3] Literally, "four-handed." In Darwin's day this name was commonly applied to apes, monkeys, and other primates except man because they use both hands and feet as grasping appendages like hands.

disuse of parts will have done much in the same direction with natural selection. Modifications formerly of importance, though no longer of any special use, are long-inherited. When one part is modified, other parts change through the principle of correlation, of which we have instances in many curious cases of correlated monstrosities. Something may be attributed to the direct and definite action of the surrounding conditions of life, such as abundant food, heat or moisture; and lastly, many characters of slight physiological [607] importance, some indeed of considerable importance, have been gained through sexual selection. . . .

Through the means just specified, aided perhaps by others as yet undiscovered, man has been raised to his present state. But since he attained to the rank of manhood, he has diverged into distinct races, or as they may be more fitly called, sub-species. Some of these, such as the Negro and European, are so distinct that, if specimens had been brought to a naturalist without any further information, they would undoubtedly have been considered by him as good and true species. Nevertheless all the races agree in so many unimportant details of structure and in so many mental peculiarities that these can be accounted for only by inheritance from a common progenitor; and a progenitor thus characterised would probably deserve to rank as man.

It must not be supposed that the divergence of each race from the other races, and of all from a common stock, can be traced back to any one pair of progenitors. On the contrary, at every stage in the process of modification, all the individuals which were in any way better fitted for their conditions of life, though in different degrees, would have survived in greater numbers than the less well-fitted. The process would have been like that followed by man, when he does not intentionally select particular individuals, but breeds from all the superior individuals, and neglects the inferior. He thus slowly but surely modifies his stock, and unconsciously forms a new strain. So with respect [608] to modifications acquired independently of selection, and due to variations arising from the nature of the organism and the action of the surrounding conditions, or from changed habits of life, no single pair will have been modified much more than the other pairs inhabiting the same country, for all will have been continually blended through free intercrossing.

By considering the embryological structure of man,—the homologies which he presents with the lower animals,—the rudiments which he retains,—and the reversions to which he is liable, we can partly recall in imagination the former condition of our early progenitors; and can approximately place them in their proper place in the zoological series. We thus learn that man is descended from a hairy, tailed quadruped, probably arboreal in its habits, and an inhabitant of the Old World. This creature, if its whole structure had been examined by a naturalist, would have been classed amongst the Quadrumana, as surely as the still more ancient progenitor of the Old and New World monkeys. The Quadrumana and all the higher mammals are probably derived from an ancient marsupial animal, and this through a long series of diversified forms, from some amphibian-like creature, and this again from some fish-like animal. In the dim obscurity of the past we can see that the early progenitor of all the Vertebrata must have been an aquatic animal provided with branchiae,[4] with the two sexes united in the same individual, and with the most important organs of the body (such as the brain and heart) imperfectly or not at all developed. This animal seems to have been more like the larvae of the existing marine Ascidians than any other known form.

The high standard of our intellectual powers and moral disposition is the greatest difficulty which presents itself, after we have been driven to this conclusion on the origin of man. But every one who admits the principle of evolution, must see that the mental powers of the higher animals, which are the same in kind with those of man, though so different in degree, are capable of advancement. Thus the interval between the mental powers of one of the higher apes and of a fish, or between those of an ant and scale-insect, is immense; yet their development does not offer any special difficulty; for with our domesticated animals, the mental faculties are certainly variable, and the variations are inherited. No one doubts that they are of the utmost importance to animals in a state of nature. Therefore the conditions are favourable for their development through natural selection. The same conclusion may be extended to man; the intellect must have been all-important to him, even at a very [609] remote period, as enabling him to invent and use language, to make weapons, tools, traps, &c., whereby with the aid of his social habits, he long ago became the most dominant of all living creatures. . . .[610] . . .

The moral nature of man has reached its present standard, partly through the advancement of his reasoning powers and consequently of a just public opinion, but especially from his sympathies having been rendered more tender and widely diffused through the effects of habit, example, instruction, and reflection. It is not improbable that after long practice virtuous tendencies may be inherited. With the more civilised races, the conviction of the existence of an all-seeing Deity has had a potent influence on the advance of morality. Ultimately man does not accept the praise or blame of his fellows as his sole guide, though few escape this influence, but his habitual convictions, controlled by reason, afford him the safest rule. His conscience then becomes the supreme judge and monitor. Nevertheless the first foundation or origin of the moral sense lies in the social instincts, including sympathy; and these instincts no doubt were primarily gained, as in the case of the lower animals, through natural selection.

---

[4] Or gills, the respiratory organs of fish and other aquatic animals.

The belief in God has often been advanced as not only the greatest, but the most complete of all the distinctions between man and the lower animals. It is however impossible, as we have seen, to maintain that this belief is innate or instinctive in man. On the other hand a belief in all-pervading spiritual agencies seems to be universal; and apparently follows from a considerable advance in man's reason, and from a still greater advance in his faculties of imagination, curiosity and wonder. I am aware that the assumed instinctive belief in God has been used by many persons as an argument for His existence. But this is a rash argument, as we should thus be compelled to believe in the existence of many cruel and malignant spirits, only a little more powerful than man; for the belief in them is far more general than in a beneficent Deity. The idea of a universal and beneficent Creator does not seem to arise in the mind of man, until he has been elevated by long-continued culture. . . .[612] . . . .

I am aware that the conclusions arrived at in this work will be denounced by some as highly irreligious; but he who denounces them is bound to shew why it is more irreligious to explain the origin of man as a distinct species by descent from some lower form, through the laws of variation and natural selection, than to explain the birth of the individual through the laws of ordinary reproduction. The birth both of the species and of the individual are equally parts of the grand sequence of events, which our minds refuse to accept as the result of blind chance. The understanding revolts at such a conclusion, whether or not we are able to believe that every slight variation of structure,—the union of each pair in marriage,—the dissemination of each seed,—and other such events, have all been ordained for some special purpose.

Sexual selection has been treated at great length in this work; for, as I have attempted to shew, it has played an important part in the history of the organic world. I am aware that much remains doubtful, but I have endeavoured to give a fair view of the whole case. In the lower divisions of the animal kingdom, sexual selection seems to have done nothing. . . . When, however, we come to the Anthropoda and Vertebrata, even to the lowest classes in these two great Sub-Kingdoms, sexual selection has effected much. . . .[613] . . . .

Sexual selection depends on the success of certain individuals over others of the same sex, in relation to the propagation of the species; whilst natural selection depends on the success of both sexes, at all ages, in relation to the general condition of life. . . .[614] . . . .

The belief in the power of sexual selection rests chiefly on the following considerations. Certain characters are confined to one sex; and this alone renders it probable that in most cases they are connected with the act of reproduction. In innumerable instances these characters are fully developed only at maturity, and often during only a part of the year, which is always the breeding-season. The males (passing over a few exceptional cases) are the more active in courtship; they are the better armed, and are rendered the more attractive in various ways. It is to be especially observed that the males display their attractions with elaborate care in the presence of the females; and that they rarely or never display them excepting during the season of love. It is incredible that all this should be purposeless. Lastly we have distinct evidence with some quadrupeds and birds, that the individuals of one sex are capable of feeling a strong antipathy or preference for certain individuals of the other sex.

Bearing in mind these facts, and the marked results of man's unconscious selection, when applied to domesticated animals and cultivated plants, it seems to me almost certain that if the individuals of one sex were during a long series of generations to prefer pairing with certain individuals of the other sex, characterised in some peculiar manner, the offspring would slowly but surely become modified in this same manner. I have not attempted to conceal that, excepting when the males are more numerous than the females, or when polygamy prevails, it is doubtful how the more attractive males succeed in leaving a [615] larger number of offspring to inherit their superiority in ornaments or other charms than the less attractive males; but I have shewn that this would probably follow from the females,—especially the more vigorous ones, which would be the first to breed,—preferring not only the more attractive but at the same time the more vigorous and victorious males. . . .[616] . . .

Man scans with scrupulous care the character and pedigree of his horses, cattle, and dogs before he matches them; but when he comes to his own marriage he rarely, or never, takes any such care. He is impelled by nearly the same motives as the lower animals, when they are left to their own free choice, though he is in so far superior to them that he highly values mental charms and virtues. On the other hand he is strongly attracted by mere wealth or rank. Yet he might by selection do something not only for the bodily constitution and frame of his offspring, but for their intellectual and moral qualities. Both sexes ought to refrain from marriage if they are in any marked degree inferior in body or mind; but such hopes are Utopian and [617] will never be even partially realised until the laws of inheritance are thoroughly known. Everyone does good service who aids towards this end. When the principles of breeding and inheritance are better understood, we shall not hear ignorant members of our legislature rejecting with scorn a plan for ascertaining whether or not consanguineous marriages are injurious to man.

The advancement of the welfare of mankind is a most intricate problem: all ought to refrain from marriage who cannot avoid abject poverty for their children; for poverty is not only a great evil, but tends to its own increase by leading to recklessness in marriage. On the other hand, as Mr. Galton [5] has remarked, if the prudent avoid marriage, whilst the reckless marry, the inferior members tend to supplant the better members of society. Man, like every other animal, has no doubt advanced to his present high condition through a struggle for existence consequent on his rapid multiplication; and if he is to advance still higher, it is to be feared that he must remain subject to a severe struggle. Otherwise he would sink into indolence, and the more gifted men would not be more successful in the battle of life than the less gifted. Hence our natural rate of increase, though leading to many and obvious evils, must not be greatly diminished by any means. There should be open competition for all men; and the most able should not be prevented by laws or customs from succeeding best and rearing the largest number of offspring. Important as the struggle for existence has been and even still is, yet as far as the highest part of man's nature is concerned there are other agencies more important. For the moral qualities are advanced, either directly or indirectly, much more through the effects of habit, the reasoning powers, instruction, religion, &c., than through natural selection; though to this latter agency may be safely attributed the social instincts, which afforded the basis for the development of the moral sense.

The main conclusion arrived at in this work, namely, that man is descended from some lowly organised form, will, I regret to think, be highly distasteful to many. But there can hardly be a doubt that we are descended from barbarians. The astonishment which I felt on first seeing a party of Feugians [6] [sic] on a wild and broken shore will never be forgotten by me, for the reflection at once rushed into my mind— such were our ancestors. These men were absolutely naked and bedaubed with paint, their long hair was tangled, their mouths frothed with excitement, and their expression was wild, startled, and distrustful.[618] They possessed hardly any arts, and like wild animals lived on what they could catch; they had no government, and were merciless to every one not of their own small tribe. He who has seen a savage in his native land will not feel much shame, if forced to acknowledge that the blood of some more humble creature flows in his veins. For my own part I would as soon be descended from that heroic little monkey, who braved his dreaded enemy in order to save the life of his keeper, or from that old baboon, who descending from the mountains, carried away in triumph his young comrade from a crowd of astonished dogs—as from a savage who delights to torture his enemies, offers up bloody sacrifices, practises infanticide without remorse, treats his wives

---

5 Francis Galton (1822-1911), English scientist and Darwin's first cousin, founder of the science of eugenics.

6 The Fuegians are aborigines of Tierra del Fuego, an archipelago off the southern coast of South America. Darwin encountered these natives while aboard the *Beagle*.

like slaves, knows no decency, and is haunted by the grossest superstitions.

Man may be excused for feeling some pride at having risen, though not through his own exertions, to the very summit of the organic scale; and the fact of his having thus risen, instead of having been aboriginally placed there, may give him hope for a still higher destiny in the distant future. But we are not here concerned with hopes or fears, only with the truth as far as our reason permits us to discover it; and I have given the evidence to the best of my ability. We must, however, acknowledge, as it seems to me, that man with all his noble qualities, with sympathy which feels for the most debased, with benevolence which extends not only to other men but to the humblest living creature, with his god-like intellect which has penetrated into the movements and constitution of the solar system—with all these exalted powers—Man still bears in his bodily frame the indelible stamp of his lowly origin.[619]

PART TWO

EARLY DEFENDERS OF DARWINISM

Organic evolution and Darwin's hypothesis of natural selection as an explanation of its mechanical operation were both ably defended by a small but distinguished group of stalwarts at home and abroad, five of whom are here represented. Joseph Hooker, one of Darwin's co-sponsors at the 1858 meeting of the Linnean Society, in the introductory essay to his *Flora of Tasmania,* published in 1859, recorded his conversion to the theory of the transmutation of species. Thomas H. Huxley, who very early became Darwin's special advocate, wrote the first important favorable review of *The Origin of Species,* in *The Times* of December 26, 1859. Asa Gray, Darwin's American correspondent and a confirmed theist, was especially concerned with showing that nothing in natural selection and evolution conflicted with traditional religion. Sir Charles Lyell, long an opponent of organic evolution, proclaimed his new faith in the Darwinian hypothesis and in transmutation. And Alfred Wallace himself, the co-formulator of the theory of natural selection, remained to the end of his life a partisan of Darwinism.

Joseph D. Hooker (1817-1911)

From the Introductory Essay to his *Flora of Tasmania* [1859]. In *The American Journal of Science and Arts,* Second Series, XXIX (January-May, 1860), 1-25, 305-326.

1. *Preliminary Remarks*

In the Introductory Essay to the New Zealand Flora, I advanced certain general propositions as to the origin of species, which I refrained from endorsing as articles of my own creed: amongst others was the still prevalent doctrine that these are, in the ordinary acceptation of the term, created as such, and are immutable. In the present Essay, I shall advance the opposite hypothesis, that species are derivative and mutable; and this chiefly because, whatever opinions a naturalist may have adopted with regard to the origin and variation of species, every candid mind must admit that the facts and arguments upon which he had grounded his convictions require revision since the recent publication by the Linnean Society of the ingenious and original reasonings and theories of Mr. Darwin and Mr. Wallace.

Further, there must be many who, like myself, having hitherto refrained from expressing any positive opinion, now, after a careful consideration of these naturalists' theories, find the aspect of the question materially changed, and themselves freer to adopt such a theory as may best harmonize with the facts adduced by their own experience. . . .[2]. . . .

With regard to my own views on the subjects of the variability of existing species and the fallacy of supposing we can ascertain anything through these alone of their ancestry or of originally created types, they are, in so far as they are liable to influence my estimate of the value of the facts collected for the analysis of the Australian Flora, unaltered from those which I maintained in the 'Flora of New Zealand.' On such theoretical questions, however, as the origin and ultimate permanence of species, they have been greatly influenced by the views and arguments of Mr. Darwin and Mr. Wallace above alluded to, which incline me to regard more favorably the hypothesis that it is to variation that we must look as the means which Nature has adopted for peopling the globe with those diverse existing forms which, when they tend to transmit their characters unchanged through many generations, are called species. . . .[4]. . . .

2. On the General Phenomena of Variation in the Vegetable Kingdom

Of . . . [the] natural groups of varying and unvarying species, some are large and some small; they are also variously distributed through the classes, orders, and genera of the Vegetable Kingdom; but, as a general rule, the varying species are relatively most numerous in those classes, orders, and genera which [6] are the simplest in structure. . . . But the prominent fact is, that this element of mutability pervades the whole vegetable kingdom; no class nor order nor genus of more than a few species claims absolute exemption, whilst the grand total of unstable forms generally assumed to be species probably exceeds that of the stable. . . .[7]. . . .

Granting . . . that the tendency of nature is first to multiply forms of existing plants by graduated changes, and next by destroying some to isolate the rest in area and in character, we are now in a condition to seek some theory of the *modus operandi* [1] of Nature that will give temporary permanence of character to these changelings. And here we must appeal to theory or speculation; for our knowledge of the history of species in relation to one another, and to the incessant mutations of their environing physical conditions, is far too limited and incomplete to afford data for demonstrating the effects of these in the production of any one species in a native state.

Of these speculations by far the most important and philosophical is that of the delimitation of species by natural selection, for which we are indebted to two wholly independent and original thinkers, Mr. Darwin and Mr. Wallace. . . .[14]. . . .

4. On the General Phenomena of the Distribution of Plants in Time

To my mind . . . the doctrine of progression, if considered in connection with the hypothesis of the origin of species being by variation, is by far the most profound of all that have ever agitated the schools of Natural History, and I do not think that it has yet been treated in the unprejudiced spirit it demands. The elements for its study are the vastest and most complicated which the naturalist can contemplate, and reside in the comprehension of the reciprocal action of the so-called inorganic on the organic world. Granting that multiplication and specialization of organs is the evidence and measure of progression, that variation explains the *rationale* of the operation which results in this progression, the question arises, What are the limits to the combinations of physical causes which determine this progression, and how can the specializing power of Nature stop short

---

[1] Manner of working.

of causing every race or variety ultimately to represent a species? . . .[312] . . . .

Before dismissing this subject, I may revert once more to the opposite doctrine, which regards species as immutable creations, and this principally to observe that the arguments in its favor have neither gained nor lost by increased facilities for investigation, or by additional means for observation. The facts are unassailable that we have no direct knowledge of the origin of any wild species; that many are separated by numerous structural peculiarities from all other plants; that some of them invariably propagate their like; and that a few have retained their characters unchanged under very different conditions and through geological epochs. Recent discoveries have not weakened the force of these facts, nor have successive thinkers derived new arguments from them; and if we hence conclude from them that species are really independent creations and immutable, though so often illimitable, then is all further inquiry a waste of time, and the question of their origin, and that of their classification in Genera and orders, can, in the present state of science, never be answered; and the only known avenues to all means of investigation must be considered as closed till the origin of life itself is brought to light. . . .[313] . . . .

It has been urged against the theory that existing species have arisen through the variation of pre-existing ones and the destruction of intermediate varieties, that it is a hasty inference from a few facts in the life of a few variable plants, and is therefore unworthy of confidence, if not of consideration; but it appears to me that the opposite theory, which demands an independent creative act for each species, is an equally hasty inference from a few negative facts in the life of certain species, of which some generations have proved invariable within our extremely limited experience. . . .[314] . . . .

The arguments deduced from genetic resemblance being (in the present state of science), as far as I can discover, exhausted, I have felt it my duty to re-examine the phenomena of variation in reference to the origin of existing species. These phenomena I have long studied independently of this question; and when treating either of whole floras or of species, I have made it my constant aim to demonstrate how much more important and prevalent this element of variability is than is usually admitted, as also how deep it lies beneath the foundations of all our facts and reasonings concerning classification and distribution. I have hitherto endeavored to keep my ideas upon variation in subjection to the hypothesis of species being immutable; both because a due regard to that theory checks any tendency to careless observation of minute facts, and because the opposite one is apt to lead to a precipitate conclusion that slight differences have no significance; whereas, though not of specific importance, they may be of high structural and physiological value, and hence reveal affinities that might otherwise escape us. I have already stated how greatly I am indebted to Mr. Darwin's [2] *rationale* of the phenomena of variation and natural selection in the production of species; and though it does not positively establish the doctrine of creation by variation, I expect that every additional fact and observation relating to species will gain great additional value from being viewed in reference to it, and that it will materially assist in developing the principles of classification and distribution.[315]. . . .

〰〰〰

Thomas H. Huxley (1825-1895)

> From "The Darwinian Hypothesis" [1859]. In *Darwiniana,* Volume II of Huxley's *Collected Essays.* London: Macmillan and Co., 1894. (Published originally as a review of Darwin's *The Origin of Species* in *The* [London] *Times,* December 26, 1859.)

The hypothesis of which the present work of Mr. Darwin is but the preliminary outline, may be stated in his own language as follows:—"Species originated by means of natural selection, or through the preservation of the favoured races in the struggle for life." To render this thesis intelligible, it is necessary to interpret its terms. In the first place, what is a species? The question is a simple one, but the right answer to it is hard to find, even if we appeal to those who should know most about it. It is all those animals or plants which have descended from a single pair of parents; it is the smallest distinctly definable group of living organisms; it is an eternal and immutable entity; it is a mere abstraction of the human intellect having no existence in nature. Such are a few of the significations attached to [1] this simple word which may be culled from authoritative sources; and if, leaving terms and theoretical subtleties aside, we turn to facts and endeavour to gather a meaning for ourselves, by studying the things to which, in practice, the name of species is applied, it profits us little. For practice varies as much as theory. Let two botanists or two zoologists examine and describe the productions of a country, and one will pretty certainly disagree with the other as to the number, limits,

---

2 In this Essay I refer to the brief abstract only (Linn. Journ.) of my friend's views, not to his work [i.e., *The Origin of Species*] now in the press, a deliberate study of which may modify my opinion on some points whereon we differ. Matured conclusions on these subjects are very slowly developed. [Hooker's note.]

and definitions of the species into which he groups the very same things. . . .

The truth is that the number of distinguishable living creatures almost surpasses imagination. . . .[2]. . . .

But is it not possible to apply a test whereby a true species may be known from a mere variety? Is there no criterion of species? Great authorities affirm that there is—that the unions of members of the same species are always fertile, while those of distinct species are either sterile, or their offspring, called hybrids, are so. It is affirmed not only that this is an experimental fact, but that it is a provision for the preservation of the purity of species. Such a criterion as this would be invaluable; but, unfortunately, not only is it not obvious how to apply it in the great majority of cases in which its aid is needed, but its general validity is stoutly denied. . . .[3]. . . .

If, weary of the endless difficulties involved in the determination of species, the investigator, contenting himself with the rough practical distinction of separable kinds, endeavours to study them as they occur in nature—to ascertain their relations to the conditions which surround them, their mutual harmonies and discordancies of structure, the bond of union of their present and their past history, he finds himself, according to the received notions, in a mighty maze, and with, at most, the dimmest adumbration of a plan. If he starts with any one clear conviction, it is that every part of a living creature is cunningly adapted to some special use in its life. . . .[4]. . . . Not only men and horses, and cats and dogs, lobsters and beetles, periwinkles and mussels, but even the very sponges and animalcules commence their existence under forms which are essentially undistinguishable; and this is true of all the infinite variety of plants. Nay, more, all living beings march, side by side, along the high road of development, and separate the later the more like they are; like people leaving church, who all go down the aisle, but having reached the door, some turn into the parsonage, others go down the village, and others part only in the next parish. A man in his development runs for a little while parallel with, though never passing through, the form of the meanest worm, then travels for a space beside the fish, then journeys along with the bird and the reptile for his fellow travelers; [5] and only at last, after a brief companionship with the highest of the four-footed and four-handed world, rises into the dignity of pure manhood. No competent thinker of the present day dreams of explaining these indubitable facts by the notion of the existence of unknown and undiscoverable adaptations to purpose. . . .[6]. . . .

But our knowledge of life is not confined to the existing world. Whatever their minor differences, geologists are agreed as to the vast thickness of the accumulated strata which compose the visible part of our earth, and the inconceivable immensity of the time the lapse of which they are the imperfect but the only accessible witnesses. . . . The naturalist finds in the bowels of the earth species as well defined as, and in some groups of animals more numerous than, those which breathe the upper air. But, singularly enough, the majority of these entombed species are wholly [8] distinct from those that now live. Nor is this unlikeness without its rule and order. As a broad fact, the further we go back in time the less the buried species are like existing forms; and, the further apart the sets of extinct creatures are, the less they are like one another. In other words, there has been a regular succession of living beings, each younger set, being in a very broad and general sense, somewhat more like those which now live.

It was once supposed that this succession had been the result of vast successive catastrophes, destructions, and re-creations *en masse;* but catastrophes are now almost eliminated from geological, or at least palaeontological speculation; and it is admitted, on all hands, that the seeming breaks in the chain of being are not absolute, but only relative to our imperfect knowledge; that species have replaced species, not in assemblages, but one by one; and that, if it were possible to have all the phenomena of the past presented to us, the convenient epochs and formations of the geologist, though having a certain distinctness, would fade into one another with limits as undefinable as those of the distinct and yet separable colours of the solar spectrum.

Such is a brief summary of the main truths which have been established concerning species. Are these truths ultimate and irresolvable facts, or are their complexities and perplexities the mere expressions of a higher law? [9]

A large number of persons practically assume the former position to be correct. They believe that the writer of the Pentateuch was empowered and commissioned to teach us scientific as well as other truth, that the account we find there of the creation of living things is simply and literally correct, and that anything which seems to contradict it is, by the nature of the case, false. All the phenomena which have been detailed are, on this view, the immediate product of a creative fiat and, consequently, are out of the domain of science altogether.

Whether this view prove ultimately to be true or false, it is, at any rate, not at present supported by what is commonly regarded as logical proof, even if it be capable of discussion by reason; and hence we consider ourselves at liberty to pass it by, and to turn to those views which profess to rest on a scientific basis only, and therefore admit of being argued to their consequences. . . .

. . . [A] majority of . . . competent persons have up to the present time maintained two positions—the first, that every species is, within certain defined limits, fixed and incapable of modification; the second, that every species was originally produced [10] by a distinct creative act. The second position is obviously incapable of proof or disproof, the direct operations of the Creator not being subjects of science; and it must therefore be regarded as a corollary from the first, the truth or falsehood of which is a matter of evidence. . . .[11]. . . .

The Lamarckian hypothesis [1] has long since been justly condemned, and it is the established practice for every tyro to raise his heel against the carcase of the dead lion. But it is rarely either wise or instructive to treat even the errors of a really great man with mere ridicule, and in the present case the logical form of the doctrine stands on a very different form from its substance. . . .[12]. . . .

Since Lamarck's time, almost all competent naturalists have left speculations on the origin of species to such dreamers as the author of the "Vestiges," [2] by whose well-intentioned efforts the Lamarckian theory received its final condemnation in the minds of all sound thinkers. Notwithstanding this silence, however, the transmutation theory, as it has been called, has been a "skeleton in the closet" to many an honest zoologist and botanist who had a soul above the mere naming of dried plants and skins. . . .[13]. . . .

Questions of this kind have assuredly often arisen, but it might have been long before they received such expression as would have commanded the respect and attention of the scientific world, had it not been for the publication of the work which prompted this article. Its author, Mr. Darwin, inheritor of a once celebrated name,[3] won his spurs in science when most of those now distinguished were young men, and has for the last twenty years held a place in the front ranks of British philosophers. . . .[14]. . . . Such a man . . . has not entered the sanctuary with unwashed hands, and when he lays before us the results of twenty years' investigation and reflection we must listen even though we be disposed to strike. But, in reading his work, it must be confessed that the attention which might at first be dutifully, soon becomes willingly, given, so clear is the author's thought, so outspoken his conviction, so honest and fair the candid expression of his doubts. Those who would judge the book must read it: we shall endeavour only to make its line of argument and its philosophical position intelligible to the general reader in our own way. . . .[15]. . . .

. . . The breeder—and a skilful one must be a person of much sagacity and natural or acquired perceptive faculty—notes some slight difference, arising he knows not how, in some individuals of his stock. If he wish to perpetuate the difference, to form a breed with the peculiarity in question strongly marked, he selects such male and female individuals as exhibit the desired character, and breeds from them. . . .[16]. . . .

---

[1] This hypothesis included as one of its features the belief in the hereditary transmission of acquired characteristics. See Introduction.

[2] Robert Chambers (1802-1871), Scottish author and publisher. In 1844 he published his *Vestiges of the Natural History of Creation* anonymously. In his argument in favor of transmutation, he anticipated Darwin's *The Origin of Species*.

[3] A reference to Erasmus Darwin (1731-1802), English scientist and poet, Charles Darwin's grandfather.

. . . Without the breeder there would be no selection, and without the selection no race. Before admitting the possibility of natural species having originated in any similar way, it must be proved that there is in Nature some power which takes the place of man, and performs a selection *suâ sponte*.[4] It is the claim of Mr. Darwin that he professes to have discovered the existence and the *modus operandi* of this "natural selection," as he terms it; and, if he be right, the process is perfectly simple and comprehensible, and irresistibly deducible from very familiar but well nigh forgotten facts.

Who, for instance, had duly reflected upon all the consequences of the marvellous struggle for existence which is daily and hourly going on among living beings? . . .[17] . . . .

Such being unquestionably the necessary conditions under which living creatures exist, Mr. Darwin discovers in them the instrument of natural selection. . . .[18] . . . .

That this most ingenious hypothesis enables us to give a reason for many apparent anomalies in the distribution of living beings in time and space,[19] and that it is not contradicted by the main phenomena of life and organisation appear to us to be unquestionable; and, so far, it must be admitted to have an immense advantage over any of its predecessors. But it is quite another matter to affirm absolutely either the truth or falsehood of Mr. Darwin's views at the present stage of the inquiry. Goethe [5] has an excellent aphorism defining that state of mind which he calls "Thätige Skepsis"—active doubt. It is doubt which so loves truth that it neither dares rest in doubting, nor extinguish itself by unjustified belief; and we commend this state of mind to students of species, with respect to Mr. Darwin's or any other hypothesis, as to their origin. The combined investigations of another twenty years may, perhaps, enable naturalists to say whether the modifying causes and the selective power, which Mr. Darwin has satisfactorily shown to exist in Nature, are competent to produce all the effects he ascribes to them; or whether, on the other hand, he has been led to over-estimate the value of the principle of natural selection, as greatly as Lamarck over-estimated his *vera causa* of modification by exercise.[6]

But there is, at all events, one advantage possessed by the more recent writer over his predecessor. Mr. Darwin abhors mere speculation as nature abhors a vacuum. He is as greedy of cases and precedents as any constitutional lawyer, and all the principles he lays down are capable of being [20] brought to the test of observation and experiment.

---

[4] Or "*sponte suâ*," of its own accord.

[5] Johann Wolfgang von Goethe (1749-1832), German philosopher, poet, dramatist, and miscellaneous writer.

[6] Another feature of the Lamarckian hypothesis was that creatures induce change in themselves by willing, or personal exercise, e.g., that giraffes developed their long necks because they wished to reach otherwise inaccessible sources of food.

The path he bids us follow professes to be, not a mere airy track, fabricated of ideal cobwebs, but a solid and broad bridge of facts. If it be so, it will carry us safely over many a chasm in our knowledge. . . .[21]

～

From "Man's Place in Nature" [1863]. In *Man's Place in Nature and other Anthropological Essays,* Volume VII of Huxley's *Collected Essays.* London: Macmillan and Co., 1894.

CHAPTER II—"ON THE RELATIONS OF MAN TO THE LOWER ANIMALS"

. . . If Man be separated by no greater structural barrier from the brutes than they are from one another—then it seems to follow that if any process of physical causation can be discovered by which the genera and families of ordinary animals have been produced, that process of causation [146] is amply sufficient to account for the origin of Man. . . .

At the present moment, but one such process of physical causation has any evidence in its favour; or, in other words, there is but one hypothesis regarding the origin of species of animals in general which has any any scientific existence—that propounded by Mr. Darwin. . . .[147]. . . .

. . . The question of the relation of man to the lower animals resolves itself, in the end, into the larger question of the tenability or untenability of Mr. Darwin's views. . . .[148]. . . .

Now, Mr. Darwin's hypothesis is not, so far as I am aware, inconsistent with any known biological fact; on the contrary, if admitted, the facts of Development, of Comparative Anatomy, of Geographical Distribution, and of Palaeontology, become connected together, and exhibit a meaning such as they never possessed before; and I, for one, am fully convinced that if not precisely true, that hypothesis is as near an approximation to the truth as, for example, the Copernican hypothesis [1] was to the true theory of the planetary motions.

But, for all this, our acceptance of the Darwinian hypothesis must be provisional so long as one link in the chain of evidence is wanting; and so long as all the animals and plants certainly produced by selective breeding from a common stock are fertile, and their progeny are fertile with one another, that link will be wanting. For, so long,

---

[1] The heliocentric conception of the planetary system developed by Nicolaus Copernicus (1473-1543), Polish astronomer.

selective breeding will not be proved to be competent to do all that is required of it to produce natural species.

I have put this conclusion as strongly as possible before the reader, because the last position [149] in which I wish to find myself is that of an advocate for Mr. Darwin's, or any other views—if by an advocate is meant one whose business it is to smooth over real difficulties, and to persuade where he cannot convince.

In justice to Mr. Darwin, however, it must be admitted that the conditions of fertility and sterility are very ill understood, and that every day's advance in knowledge leads us to regard the hiatus in his evidence as of less and less importance, when set against the multitude of facts which harmonize with, or receive an explanation from, his doctrines.

I adopt Mr. Darwin's hypothesis, therefore, subject to the production of proof that physiological species may be produced by selective breeding; just as a physical philosopher may accept the undulatory theory of light, subject to the proof of the existence of the hypothetical ether; or as the chemist adopts the atomic theory, subject to the proof of the existence of atoms; and for exactly the same reasons, namely, that it has an immense amount of primâ facie probability; that it is the only means at present within reach of reducing the chaos of observed facts to order; and lastly, that it is the most powerful instrument of investigation which has been presented to naturalists since the invention of the natural system of classification and the commencement of the systematic study of embryology.[150]

But even leaving Mr. Darwin's views aside, the whole analogy of natural operations furnishes so complete and crushing an argument against the intervention of any but what are termed secondary causes, in the production of all the phenomena of the universe; that, in view of the intimate relations between Man and the rest of the living world, and between the forces exerted by the latter and all other forces, I can see no excuse for doubting that all are co-ordinated terms of Nature's great progression, from the formless to the formed—from the inorganic to the organic—from blind force to conscious intellect and will. . . .[151] . . .

From "Criticisms on 'The Origin of Species'"
[1864]. In *Darwiniana*.

Teleology implies that the organs of every organism are perfect and cannot be improved; the Darwinian theory simply affirms that they work [84] well enough to enable the organism to hold its own against such competitors as it has met with, but admits the possibility of indefinite improvement. But an example may bring into clearer light the profound opposition between the ordinary teleological, and the Darwinian, conception.

Cats catch mice, small birds and the like, very well. Teleology tells us that they do so because they were expressly constructed for so doing —that they are perfect mousing apparatuses, so perfect and so delicately adjusted that no one of their organs could be altered, without the change involving the alteration of all the rest. Darwinism affirms on the contrary, that there was no express construction concerned in the matter; but that among the multitudinous variations of the Feline stock, many of which died out from want of power to resist opposing influences, some, the cats, were better fitted to catch mice than others, whence they throve and persisted, in proportion to the advantage over their fellows thus offered to them.

Far from imagining that cats exist *in order* to catch mice well, Darwinism supposes that cats exist *because* they catch mice well— mousing being not the end, but the condition, of their existence. And if the cat type has long persisted as we know it, the interpretation of the fact upon the Darwinian principles would be, not that the cats have remained invariable, but that such varieties as have incessantly occurred have been, on the whole, less [85] fitted to get on in the world than the existing stock.

If we apprehend the spirit of the "Origin of Species" rightly, then, nothing can be more entirely and absolutely opposed to Teleology, as it is commonly understood, than the Darwinian Theory. . . .[86]. . . .

From "The Coming of Age of 'The Origin of Species.'" In *Darwiniana*. (Originally a lecture delivered at the Royal Institution on April 9, 1880.)

Many of you will be familiar with the aspect of this small green-covered book. It is a copy of the first edition of the "Origin of Species," and bears the date of its production—the 1st of October 1859. Only a few months, therefore, are needed to complete the full tale of twenty-one years since its birthday.

Those whose memories carry them back to this time will remember that the infant was remarkably lively, and that a great number of excellent persons mistook its manifestations of a vigorous individuality for mere naughtiness; in fact there was very pretty turmoil about its cradle. My recollections of the period are particularly vivid; for, having conceived a tender affection for a child of what appeared to me such remarkable promise, I acted for some time in the capacity of a [227] sort of under-nurse, and thus came in for my share of the storms which threatened the very life of the young creature. For some years it was undoubtedly warm work; but considering how exceedingly unpleasant the apparition of the newcomer must have been to those who did not fall in love with him at first sight, I think it is to the credit of our age that the war was not fiercer, and that the more bitter and unscrupulous forms of opposition died away as soon as they did.

I speak of this period as of something past and gone, possessing merely an historical, I had almost said an antiquarian interest. For, during the second decade of the existence of the "Origin of Species," opposition, though by no means dead, assumed a different aspect. On the part of all those who had any reason to respect themselves, it assumed a thoroughly respectful character. By this time, the dullest began to perceive that the child was not likely to perish of any congenital weakness or infantile disorder, but was growing into a stalwart personage, upon whom mere goody scoldings and threatenings with the birch-rod were quite thrown away.

In fact, those who have watched the progress of science within the last ten years will bear me out to the full, when I assert that there is no field of biological inquiry in which the influence of the "Origin of Species" is not traceable; the foremost men of science in every country are either avowed [228] champions of its leading doctrines, or at any rate abstain from opposing them; a host of young and ardent investigators seek for and find inspiration and guidance in Mr. Darwin's great work; and the general doctrine of evolution, to one side of which it gives expression, obtains, in the phenomena of biology, a firm base of operations whence it may conduct its conquest of the whole realm of Nature. . . . [229] . . . .

One-and-twenty years ago, in spite of the work commenced by Hutton [1] and continued with rare skill and patience by Lyell, the dominant view of the past history of the earth was catastrophic. Great and sudden physical revolutions, wholesale creations and extinctions of living beings, were the ordinary machinery of the geological epic brought into fashion by the misapplied genius of Cuvier.[2] It was gravely maintained and taught that the end of every geological epoch was signalised by a cataclysm, by which every living being on the globe was swept away, to be replaced by a brand-new creation when the world returned to quiescence. . . .

I may be wrong, but I doubt if, at the present time, there is a single responsible representative of these opinions left. . . . [231] . . . .

To those who are familiar with the process of development, all *à priori* objections to the doctrine of biological evolution appear child-

---

[1] James Hutton (1726-1797), Scottish geologist.

[2] Georges Léopold Chrétien Frédéric Dagobert, Baron Cuvier (1769-1832), French zoologist and geologist, who championed the theory of catastrophism.

ish. Any one who has watched the gradual formation of a complicated animal from the protoplasmic mass, which constitutes the essential element of a frog's or a hen's egg, has had under his eyes sufficient evidence that a similar evolution of the whole animal world from the like foundation is, at any rate, possible. . . .[238]. . . .

. . . I venture to repeat what I have said before, that so far as the animal world is concerned, evolution is no longer a speculation, but a statement of historical fact. It takes its place alongside of those accepted truths which must be reckoned with by philosophers of all schools.

Thus when, on the first day of October next, "The Origin of Species" comes of age, the promise of its youth will be amply fulfilled; and we [242] shall be prepared to congratulate the venerated author of the book, not only that the greatness of his achievement and its enduring influence upon the progress of knowledge have won him a place beside our Harvey; [3] but, still more, that, like Harvey, he has lived long enough to outlast detraction and opposition, and to see the stone that the builder rejected become the head-stone of the corner.[243]

⁀⁀⁀⁀⁀⁀⁀

Asa Gray (1810-1888)

From "Natural Selection Not Inconsistent with Natural Theology" [1860]. In *Darwiniana: Essays and Reviews Pertaining to Darwinism*. New York: D. Appleton and Co., 1884.

. . . It is undeniable that Mr. Darwin has purposely been silent upon the philosophical and theological applications of his theory. This reticence, under the circumstances, argues design, and raises inquiry as to the final cause or reason why. Here, as in higher instances, confident as we are that there is a final cause, we must not be over-confident that we can infer the particular or true one. Perhaps the author is more familiar with natural-historical than with philosophical inquiries, and, not having decided which particular theory about efficient cause is best founded, he meanwhile argues the scientific questions concerned—all that relates to secondary causes—upon purely scientific grounds, as he must do in any case. Perhaps, confident, as he evidently is, that his

---

[3] William Harvey (1578-1657), English physician and anatomist, discoverer of the circulation of the blood.

view will finally be adopted, he may enjoy a sort of satisfaction in hearing it denounced as sheer atheism by the inconsiderate, and afterward, when it takes its place with the nebular hypothesis and the like, see this judgment reversed, as we suppose it would be in such event.

Whatever Mr. Darwin's philosophy may be, or whether he has any, is a matter of no consequence at all, compared with the important questions, whether a theory to account for the origination and diversification [144] of animal and vegetable forms through the operation of secondary causes does or does not exclude design; and whether the establishment by adequate evidence of Darwin's particular theory of diversification through variation and natural selection would essentially alter the present scientific and philosophical grounds for theistic views of Nature. . . . After full and serious consideration, we are constrained to say that, in our opinion, the adoption of a derivative hypothesis, and of Darwin's particular hypothesis, if we understand it, would leave the doctrines of final causes, utility, and special design, just where they were before. We do not pretend that the subject is not environed with difficulties. Every view is so environed; and every shifting of the view is likely, if it removes some difficulties, to bring others into prominence. But we cannot perceive that Darwin's theory brings in any new kind of scientific difficulty, that is, any with which philosophical naturalists were not already familiar.

Since natural science deals only with secondary or natural causes, the scientific terms of a theory of derivation of species—no less than of a theory of dynamics—must needs be the same to the theist as to the atheist. The difference appears only when the inquiry is carried up to the question of primary cause—a question which belongs to philosophy. Wherefore, Darwin's reticence about efficient cause does not disturb us. He considers only the scientific questions. As [145] already stated, we think that a theistic view of Nature is implied in his book, and we must charitably refrain from suggesting the contrary until the contrary is logically deduced from his premises. . . .[146] . . .

To insist, therefore, that the new hypothesis of the derivative origin of the actual species is incompatible with final causes and design, is to take a position which [148] we must consider philosophically untenable. We must also regard it as highly unwise and dangerous, in the present state and present prospects of physical and physiological science. We should expect the philosophical atheist or skeptic to take this ground; also, until better informed, the unlearned and unphilosophical believer; but we should think that the thoughtful theistic philosopher would take the other side. Not to do so seems to concede that only supernatural events can be shown to be designed, which no theist can admit—seems also to misconceive the scope and meaning of all ordinary arguments for design in Nature. . . . At least, Mr. Darwin uses expressions which imply that the natural forms which surround us, because they have a history or natural sequence, could have been only generally, but not particularly designed—a view at once superficial and contradictory; whereas his true line should be, that his hypothesis concerns the *order* and not the *cause*, the *how*, and not the *why* of the phenomena, and so leaves the question of design just where it was before. . . .[149]

The whole argument in natural theology proceeds upon the ground that the inference for a final cause of the structure of the hand and of the valves in the veins is just as valid now, in individuals produced through natural generation, as it would have been in the case of the first man, supernaturally created. Why not, then, just as good even on the supposition of the descent of men from chimpanzees and gorillas, since those animals possess these same contrivances? . . . [150]. . . .

We could not affirm that the arguments for design in Nature are conclusive to all minds. But we may insist, upon grounds already intimated, that, whatever they were good for before Darwin's book appeared, they are good for now. To our minds the argument from design always appeared conclusive of the being and continued operation of an intelligent First Cause, the Ordainer of Nature; and we do not see that the grounds of such belief would be disturbed or shifted by the adoption of Darwin's hypothesis.. We are not [152] blind to the philosophical difficulties which the thoroughgoing implication of design in Nature has to encounter, nor is it our vocation to obviate them. It suffices us to know that they are not new nor peculiar difficulties— that, as Darwin's theory and our reasonings upon it did not raise these perturbing spirits, they are not bound to lay them. Meanwhile, that the doctrine of design encounters the very same difficulties in the material that it does in the moral world is just what ought to be expected.

So the issue between the skeptic and the theist is only the old one, long ago argued out—namely, whether organic Nature is the result of design or of chance. Variation and natural selection open no third alternative; they concern only the question how the results, whether fortuitous or designed, may have been brought about. Organic Nature abounds with unmistakable and irresistible indications of design, and, being a connected and consistent system, this evidence carries the implication of design throughout the whole. On the other hand, chance carries no probabilities with it, can never be developed into a consistent system, but, when applied to the explanation of orderly or beneficial results, heaps up improbabilities at every step beyond all computation. To us, a fortuitous Cosmos is simply inconceivable. The alternative is a designed Cosmos. . . .[153]. . . .

The argument for the permanence of species, drawn from the identity with those now living of cats, birds, and other animals preserved in Egyptian catacombs, was good enough as used by Cuvier [1] against

---

[1] See p. 50, footnote 2.

St.-Hilaire,[2] that is, against the supposition that time brings about a gradual alteration of whole species; but it goes for little against Darwin, unless it be proved that species never vary, or that the perpetuation of a variety necessitates the extinction of a parent breed. For Darwin clearly maintains—what the facts warrant—that the mass of a species remains fixed so long as it exists at all, though it may set off a variety now and then. The variety may finally supersede the parent form, or it may coexist with it; yet it does not in the least hinder the unvaried stock from continuing true to the breed, unless it crosses with it. The common [174] law of inheritance may be expected to keep both the original and the variety mainly true as long as they last, and none the less so because they have given rise to occasional varieties. . . .

. . . We advise nobody to accept Darwin's or any other derivative theory as true. The time has not come for that, and perhaps never will. We also advise against a similar credulity on the other side, in a blind faith that species—that the manifold sorts and forms of existing animals and vegetables—"have no secondary cause." The contrary is already not unlikely, and we suppose will hereafter become more and more probable. But we are confident that, if a derivative hypothesis ever is established, it will be so on a solid theistic ground.

Meanwhile an inevitable and legitimate hypothesis is on trial—an hypothesis thus far not untenable—a [175] trial just now very useful to science, and, we conclude, not harmful to religion, unless injudicious assailants temporarily make it so.

One good effect is already manifest; its enabling the advocates of the hypothesis of a multiplicity of human species to perceive the double insecurity of their ground. When the races of men are admitted to be of one *species,* the corollary, that they are of one *origin,* may be expected to follow. Those who allow them to be of one species must admit an actual diversification into strongly-marked and persistent varieties, and so admit the basis of fact upon which the Darwinian hypothesis is built; while those, on the other hand, who recognize several or numerous human species, will hardly be able to maintain that such species were primordial and supernatural in the ordinary sense of the word.

The English mind is prone to positivism and kindred forms of materialistic philosophy, and we must expect the derivative theory to be taken up in that interest. We have no predilection for that school, but the contrary. If we had, we might have looked complacently upon a line of criticism which would indirectly, but effectively, play into the hands of positivists and materialistic atheists generally. The wiser and stronger ground to take is, that the derivative hypothesis leaves the argument for design, and therefore for a designer, as valid as it ever was; that to do any work by an instrument must require, and there-

---

[2] Étienne Geoffroy Saint-Hilaire (1772-1844), French zoologist.

fore presuppose, the exertion rather of more than of less power than to do it directly; that whoever would be a consistent theist should believe that Design in the natural [176] world is coextensive with Providence, and hold as firmly to the one as he does to the other, in spite of the wholly similar and apparently insuperable difficulties which the mind encounters whenever it endeavors to develop the idea into a system, either in the material and organic, or in the moral world. It is enough, in the way of obviating objections, to show that the philosophical difficulties of the one are the same, and only the same, as of the other.[177]

⁀⁀⁀

Charles Lyell (1797-1875)

> From *The Geological Evidences of the Antiquity of Man*. 4th ed. London: John Murray, 1873. (Published originally in 1863.)

PART III

The Origin of Species as Bearing upon Man's Place in Nature

CHAPTER XX—"THEORIES OF PROGRESSION AND TRANSMUTATION"

While, in 1832, I argued against Lamarck's doctrine of the gradual transmutation of one species into another, I agreed with him in believing that the system of changes now in progress in the organic world would afford, when fully understood, a complete key to the interpretation of all the vicissitudes of the living creation in past ages. I contended against the doctrine, then very popular, of the sudden destruction of vast multitudes of species, and the abrupt ushering into the world of new batches of plants and animals. . . .[439] . . . .

But while rejecting transmutation, I was equally opposed to the popular theory that the creative power had diminished in energy, or that it had been in abeyance ever since Man had entered upon the scene. That a renovating force, which had been in full operation for millions of years, should cease to act while the causes of extinction were still in full activity, or even intensified by the accession of Man's destroying power, seemed to me in the highest degree improbable. The only point on which I doubted was, whether the force might not be intermittent instead of being, as Lamarck supposed, in [440] ceaseless operation. . . .[441] . . . .

CHAPTER XXI—"ON THE ORIGIN OF SPECIES BY VARIATION AND
                    NATURAL SELECTION"

Independent Creation

When I formerly advocated the doctrine that species were primordial creations, and not derivative, I endeavoured to explain the manner
of their geographical distribution, and the affinity of living forms to
the fossil types nearest akin to them in the tertiary strata of the same
part of the globe, by supposing that the creative power, which originally
adapts certain types to aquatic and others to terrestrial conditions, has,
at successive geological epochs, introduced new forms best suited to
each area and climate, so as to fill the places of those which may have
died out.

In that case, although the new species would differ from the old
(for these would not be revived, having been already proved, by the
fact of their extinction, to be incapable of holding their ground),
still, they would resemble their predecessors generically. For, as Mr.
Darwin states in regard to new races, those of a dominant type inherit
the advantages which made their parent species flourish in the same
country, and they likewise partake in those general advantages which
made the genus to which the parent species belonged, a large genus
in its own country.

We might, therefore, by parity of reasoning, have anticipated that
the creative power, adapting the new types to the new combination of
organic and inorganic conditions of a given region, such as its soil,
climate, and inhabitants, would [469] introduce new modifications of
the old types,—marsupials, for example, in Australia, new sloths and
armadilloes in South America, new heaths at the Cape, new roses in
the northern and new calceolaries [1] in the southern hemisphere. But
to this line of argument Mr. Darwin and Dr. Hooker reply, that when
animals or plants migrate into new countries, whether assisted by
man, or without his aid, the most successful colonisers appertain by
no means to those types which are most allied to the old indigenous
species. On the contrary, it more frequently happens that members
of genera, orders, or even classes, distinct and foreign to the invaded
country, make their way most rapidly, and become dominant at the
expense of the endemic species. . . . Hence, the transmutationists
infer that, the reason why these foreign types, so peculiarly fitted for
these regions, have never before been developed there, is simply that
they were excluded by natural barriers. But these barriers of sea, or
desert, or mountain, could never have been of the least avail, had the
creative force acted independently of material laws, or had it not
pleased the Author of Nature that the origin of new species should
be governed by some secondary causes analogous to those which we

---

[1] Tropical American plants of the figwort family.

see preside over the appearance of new varieties, which never appear except as the offspring of a parent stock very closely resembling them.[470]

CHAPTER XXIV–"BEARING OF THE DOCTRINE OF TRANSMUTATION ON THE ORIGIN OF MAN, AND HIS PLACE IN THE CREATION"

Some of the opponents of transmutation, who are well versed in Natural History admit that though they consider the doctrine to be untenable, it is not without its practical advantages as a 'useful working hypothesis,' suggesting good experiments and observations, and aiding us to retain in the memory a multitude of facts respecting the geographical distribution of genera and species, both of animals and plants, and the succession in time of organic remains, and many other phenomena which, but for such a theory, would be wholly without a common bond of relationship.

It is in fact conceded by many eminent zoologists and [521] botanists as before explained, that whatever may be the nature of the species-making power or law, its effects are of such a character as to imitate the results which variation, guided by natural selection, would produce, if only we could assume with certainty that there are no limits to the variability of species. But as the anti-transmutationists are persuaded that such limits do exist, they regard the hypothesis as simply a provisional one, and expect that it will one day be superseded by another cognate theory, which will not require us to assume the former continuousness of the links which have connected the past and present states of the organic world, or the outgoing with the incoming species. . . .

But will not transmutation, if adopted, require us to include the human race in the same continuous series of developments, so that we must hold that Man himself has been derived by an unbroken line of descent from some one [522] of the inferior animals? Mr. Darwin, in his late work on the 'Descent of Man,' has said, in reply to this question, that 'the similarity between man and the lower animals in embryonic development as well as in innumerable points of structure and constitution—the rudiments which he retains and the abnormal reversions to which he is occasionally liable—are facts which cannot be disputed. . . . All [the facts] point in the plainest manner to the conclusion that man is the co-descendant with other mammals of a common progenitor.'

We certainly cannot escape from such a conclusion without abandoning many of the weightiest arguments which have been urged in support of variation and natural selection, considered as the subordinate causes by which new types have been gradually introduced into the earth. . . .[523] . . .

Absence of Intermediate Fossil Anthropomorphous Species

The opponents of the theory of transmutation sometimes argue that, if there had been a passage by variation from the lower Primates to Man, the geologist ought ere this to have detected some fossil remains of the intermediate links of the chain. But what we have said respecting the absence of gradational forms between the recent and pliocene [2] mammalia . . . may serve to show the weakness in the present state of science of any argument based on such negative evidence, especially in the case of Man, since we have not yet searched those pages of the great book of nature, in which alone we have any right to expect to find records of the missing links alluded to. . . .

At some future day, when many hundred species of extinct quadrumana may have been brought to light, the naturalist may speculate with advantage on this subject; at present we must be content to wait patiently, and not to allow our judgment respecting transmutation to be influenced by the want of evidence, which it would be contrary to analogy to look [538] for in pleistocene [3] deposits in any districts, which as yet we have carefully examined. For, as we meet with extinct kangaroos and wombats in Australia, extinct llamas and sloths in South America, so in equatorial Africa, and in certain islands of the East Indian Archipelago, may we hope to meet hereafter with lost types of the anthropoid Primates, allied to the gorilla, chimpanzee, and orang-outang. . . . [539] . . . .

Transmutation and Natural Theology

. . . Dr. Asa Gray . . . has pointed out that there is no tendency in the doctrine of Variation and Natural Selection to weaken the foundations of Natural Theology; for, consistently with the derivative hypothesis of species, we may hold any of the popular views respecting the manner in which the changes of the natural world are brought about. . . . They who maintain that the origin of an individual, as well as the origin of a species or a genus, can be explained only by the direct action of the creative cause, may retain their favourite theory compatibly with the doctrine of transmutation. . . . [551] . . . .

As to the charge of materialism brought against all forms of the development theory, Dr. Gray has done well to remind us that 'of the two great minds of the seventeenth century, Newton [4] and Leibnitz, both profoundly religious as well as philosophical, one produced the theory of gravitation, the other objected to that theory that it was subversive of natural religion.' [5]

---

[2] The three latest epochs of geological time, beginning with the most recent, are the Recent, the Pleistocene, and the Pliocene. See Glossary.

[3] See footnote 2 above.

[4] Sir Isaac Newton (1642-1727), English mathematician, physicist, natural philosopher, and discoverer of the law of gravitation.

[5] See p. 25.

It may be said that, so far from having a materialistic tendency, the supposed introduction into the earth at successive geological periods of life,—sensation,—instinct,—the intelligence of the higher mammalia bordering on reason,—and lastly, the improvable reason of Man himself, presents us with a picture of the ever-increasing dominion of mind over matter.[552]

⌇

> From *Principles of Geology, or the Modern Changes of the Earth and its Inhabitants Considered as Illustrative of Geology.* Volume II. 11th ed. New York: D. Appleton and Co., 1872. (Published originally in 1830-33. The tenth edition of 1866-68 was the first to appear after the publication of Darwin's *The Origin of Species.*)

CHAPTER XXXV—"THEORIES AS TO THE NATURE OF SPECIES, AND DARWIN ON NATURAL SELECTION"

In former editions of this work from 1832 to 1853, I did not venture to differ from the opinion of Linnæus [1] that each species had remained from its origin such as we now see it, being variable, but only within certain fixed limits. The mystery in which the origin of each species was involved seemed to me no greater than that in which the beginning of all vital phenomena on the earth is shrouded. But I undertook to show that the gradual extinction of species one after another was part of the constant and regular course of nature, and must have been so throughout all geological time, because the climate, and the position of land and sea, and all the principal conditions of the organic and inorganic world, are always, and have been always, undergoing change. I pointed out how the struggle for existence among species, and the increase and spread of some of them, must tend to the extermination of others; and as these would disappear gradually and singly from the scene, I suggested [269] that probably the coming in of new species would in like manner be successive, and that there was no geological sanction for the favourite doctrine of some theorists, that large assemblages of new forms had been ushered in at once to compensate for the sudden removal of many others from the scene. . . .[270]. . . .

. . . Speaking generally, it may be said that all the most influential teachers of geology, paleontology, zoology, and botany continued

---

[1] Carolus Linnaeus, or Carl von Linné (1707-1778), Swedish botanist and founder of modern systematic biology.

till near the middle of this century either to assume the independent creation and immutability of species, or carefully to avoid expressing any opinion on this important subject. In England the calm was first broken by the appearance in 1844 of a work entitled 'The Vestiges of Creation,' [2] in which the anonymous author had gathered [274] together and presented to the public, with great clearness and skill, the new facts brought to light in geology and the kindred sciences since the time of Lamarck in favour of the transmutation of species and their progressive development in time. . . .[275]. . . .

. . . The abandonment of the old received doctrine of the 'immutability of species' was accelerated in England by the appearance, in the same year (1859),[3] of Dr. Hooker's essay on the Flora of Australia.[4] . . .[282]. . . .

CHAPTER XLIII—"MAN CONSIDERED WITH REFERENCE TO HIS ORIGIN AND GEOGRAPHICAL DISTRIBUTION"

Was Lamarck right, assuming progressive development to be true, in supposing that the changes of the organic world may have been effected by the gradual and insensible modification of older pre-existing forms? Mr. Darwin, without absolutely proving this, has made it appear in the highest degree probable, by an appeal to many distinct and independent classes of phenomena in natural history and geology, but principally by showing the manner in which a multitude of new and competing varieties are always made to survive in the struggle for life. The tenor of his reasoning is not to be gainsaid by affirming that the causes or processes which bring about the improvement or differentiation of organs, and the general advance of the [499] organic world from the simpler to the more complex, remain as inscrutable to us as ever.

When first the doctrine of the origin of species by transmutation was proposed, it was objected that such a theory substituted a material self-adjusting machinery for a Supreme Creative Intelligence. But the more the idea of a slow and insensible change from lower to higher organisms, brought about in the course of millions of generations according to a preconceived plan, has become familiar to men's minds, the more conscious they have become that the amount of power, wisdom, design, or forethought, required for such a gradual evolution of life, is as great as that which is implied by a multitude of separate, special, and miraculous acts of creation.

A more serious cause of disquiet and alarm arises out of the supposed bearing of this same doctrine on the origin of man and his

---

[2] See p. 45, footnote 2.

[3] The same year, that is, in which Darwin published *The Origin of Species*.

[4] Also identified as the Introductory Essay to the *Flora of Tasmania*. See pp. 39-42.

place in nature. It is clearly seen that there is such a close affinity, such an identity in all essential points, in our corporeal structure and in many of our instincts and passions, with those of the lower animals —that man is so completely subjected to the same general laws of reproduction, increase, growth, disease, and death,—that if progressive development, spontaneous variation, and natural selection have for millions of years directed the changes of the rest of the organic world, we cannot expect to find that the human race has been exempted from the same continuous process of evolution. Such a near bond of connection between man and the rest of the animate creation is regarded by many as derogatory to our dignity. It certainly gives a rude shock to many traditional beliefs, and dispels some poetic illusions respecting an ideal genealogy which scarcely 'appeared less than arch-angel ruined.' But we have already had to exchange the pleasing conceptions indulged in by poets and theologians as to the high position in the scale of being held by our early progenitors, for more humble and lowly beginnings, the joint labours of the geologist and archaeologist having left us in no doubt of the ignorance and barbarism of Paleolithic Man.[500]

We are sometimes tempted to ask whether the time will ever arrive, when science shall have obtained such an ascendancy in the education of the millions, that it will be possible to welcome new truths, instead of always looking upon them with fear and disquiet, and to hail every important victory gained over error, instead of resisting the new discovery, long after the evidence in its favour is conclusive. The motion of our planet round the sun, the shape of the earth, the existence of the antipodes, the vast antiquity of our globe, the distinct assemblages of species of animals and plants by which it was successively inhabited, and lastly the antiquity and barbarism of Primeval Man, all these generalisations, when first announced, have been a source of anxiety and unhappiness. The future now opening before us begins already to reveal new doctrines, if possible more than ever out of harmony with cherished associations of thought. It is therefore desirable, when we contrast ourselves with the rude and superstitious savages who preceded us, to remember, as cultivators of science, that the high comparative place which we have reached in the scale of being has been gained step by step by a conscientious study of natural phenomena, and by fearlessly teaching the doctrines to which they point. It is by faithfully weighing evidence, without regard to preconceived notions, by earnestly and patiently searching for what is true, not what we wish to be true, that we have attained that dignity, which we may in vain hope to claim through the rank of an ideal parentage.[501]

Alfred Russel Wallace (1823-1913)

> From "Creation by Law" [1868]. In *Natural Selection and Tropical Nature—Essays on Descriptive and Theoretical Biology.* New ed. London: Macmillan and Co., 1891. Reprinted by permission of A. J. R. Wallace.

Among the various criticisms that have appeared on Mr. Darwin's celebrated *Origin of Species,* there is, perhaps, none that will appeal to so large a number of well educated and intelligent persons as that contained in the Duke of Argyll's [1] *Reign of Law.* The noble author represents the feelings and expresses the ideas of that large class of persons who take a keen interest in the progress of science in general, and especially that of Natural History, but have never themselves studied nature in detail, or acquired that personal knowledge of the structure of closely allied forms,—the wonderful gradations from species to species and from group to group, and the infinite variety of the phenomena of "variation" in organic beings,—which is absolutely necessary for a full appreciation of the facts and reasonings contained in Mr. Darwin's great work.

Nearly half of the Duke's book is devoted to an exposition of his idea of "Creation by Law," and he expresses so clearly what are his difficulties and objections as regards the theory of "Natural Selection," that I think it advisable that they should be fairly answered, and that his own views should be shown to lead to conclusions as hard to accept as any which he imputes to Mr. Darwin.

The point on which the Duke of Argyll lays most stress is, that proofs of Mind everywhere meet us in Nature, and are more especially manifest wherever we find "contrivance" or "beauty." He maintains that this indicates the constant [141] supervision and direct interference of the Creator, and cannot possibly be explained by the unassisted action of any combination of laws. Now, Mr. Darwin's work has for its main object to show that all the phenomena of living things,—all their wonderful organs and complicated structures, their infinite variety of form, size, and colour, their intricate and involved relations to each other,—may have been produced by the action of a few general laws of the simplest kinds, laws which are in most cases mere statements of admitted facts. The chief of these laws or facts are the following:—

---

[1] George John Douglas Campbell, 8th Duke of Argyll (1823-1900), English statesman and writer.

1. *The Law of Multiplication in Geometrical Progression. . . .*
2. *The Law of Limited Population. . . .*
3. *The Law of Heredity, or Likeness of Offspring to their Parents. . . .*
4. *The Law of Variation. . . .*[142] *. . . .*
5. *The Law of unceasing Change of Physical Conditions upon the Surface of the Earth. . . .*
6. *The Equilibrium or Harmony of Nature.*—When a species is well adapted to the conditions which environ it, it flourishes; when imperfectly adapted it decays; when ill-adapted it becomes extinct. If *all* the conditions which determine an organism's wellbeing are taken into consideration, this statement can hardly be disputed.

This series of facts or laws are mere statements of what is the condition of nature. They are facts or inferences which are generally known, generally admitted—but, in discussing the subject of the "Origin of Species," as generally forgotten. It is from these universally admitted facts that the origin of all the varied forms of nature may be deduced by a logical chain of reasoning, which, however, is at every step verified and shown to be in strict accord with facts; and, at the same time, many curious phenomena which can by no other means be understood are explained and accounted for. It is probable that these primary facts or laws are but results of the very nature of life, and of the essential properties of organised and unorganised matter. . . . The question then is—whether the variety, the harmony, the contrivance, and the beauty we perceive in organic beings can have been produced by the action of these laws alone, or whether we are required to believe in the incessant interference and direct action of the mind and will of the Creator. It is simply a question of how the Creator has worked. The Duke (and I quote him as having well expressed the views of the more intelligent of Mr. Darwin's opponents) maintains that He has personally applied general laws to produce effects [143] which those laws are not in themselves capable of producing; that the universe alone, with all its laws intact, would be a sort of chaos, without variety, without harmony, without design, without beauty; that there is not (and therefore we may presume that there could not be) any self-developing power in the universe. I believe, on the contrary, that the universe is so constituted as to be self-regulating; that as long as it contains Life, the forms under which that life is manifested have an inherent power of adjustment to each other and to surrounding nature; and that this adjustment necessarily leads to the greatest amount of variety and beauty and enjoyment, because it does depend on general laws, and not on a continual supervision and rearrangement of details. As a matter of feeling and religion, I hold this to be a far higher conception of the Creator and of the Universe than that which may be called the "continual interference" hypothesis;

but it is not a question to be decided by our feelings or convictions—
it is a question of facts and of reason. Could the change which geology
shows us has continually taken place in the forms of life, have been
produced by general laws, or does it imperatively require the incessant
supervision of a creative mind? This is the question for us to consider,
and our opponents have the difficult task of proving a negative, if we
show that there are both facts and analogies in our favour. . . . [144] . . . .

How New Forms are Produced by Variation and Selection

. . . The Duke of Argyll sets forth his idea of creation as a
"creation by birth," but maintains that each birth of a new form
from parents differing from itself has been produced by a special
interference of the Creator, in order to direct the process of development into certain channels; that each new species is in fact a "special
creation," although brought into existence through the ordinary laws
of reproduction. He maintains, therefore, that the laws of multiplication and variation cannot furnish the right kinds of materials at the
right times for natural selection to work on. I believe, on the contrary, that it can be logically *proved* from the six axiomatic laws before
laid down, that such materials would be furnished; but I prefer to
show there are abundance of *facts* which demonstrate that they are
furnished.

The experience of all cultivators of plants and breeders of animals
shows that, when a sufficient number of individuals are examined,
variations of any required kind can always be [156] met with. On this
depends the possibility of obtaining breeds, races, and fixed varieties
of animals and plants; and it is found that any one form of variation
may be accumulated by selection, without materially affecting the
other characters of the species; . . .

. . . If we want any special quality in any animal we have only
to breed it in sufficient quantities and watch carefully, and the required variety is *always* found, and can be increased to almost any
desired extent. . . . [157] . . .

Conclusion

I have thus endeavoured to meet fairly, and to answer plainly, a
few of the most common objections to the theory of natural selection,
and I have done so in every case by referring to admitted facts and to
logical deductions from these facts.

As an indication and general summary of the line of argument I
have adopted, I here give a brief demonstration in a tabular form of
the Origin of Species by means of Natural Selection, referring for the
facts to Mr. Darwin's works, and to the pages in this volume, where
they are more or less fully treated.

A Demonstration of the Origin of Species by Natural Selection

PROVED FACTS	NECESSARY CONSEQUENCES
	(afterwards taken as Proved Facts)

RAPID INCREASE OF ORGANISMS, pp. 23, 142 (*Origin of Species*, p. 75, 5th ed.) TOTAL NUMBER OF INDIVIDUALS STATIONARY, p. 23.	STRUGGLE FOR EXISTENCE, the deaths equalling the births on the average, p. 24 (*Origin of Species*, chap. iii.)
STRUGGLE FOR EXISTENCE. HEREDITY WITH VARIATION, or general likeness with individual differences of parents and offsprings, pp. 142, 156, 179 (*Origin of Species*, chaps. i. ii. v.)	SURVIVAL OF THE FITTEST, or Natural Selection; meaning, simply, that on the whole those die who are least fitted to maintain their existence (*Origin of Species*, chap. iv.)
SURVIVAL OF THE FITTEST. CHANGE OF EXTERNAL CONDITIONS, universal and unceasing. — See Lyell's *Principles of Geology*.	CHANGES OF ORGANIC FORMS, to keep them in harmony with the Changed Conditions; and as the changes of conditions are permanent changes, in the sense of not reverting back to identical previous conditions, the changes of organic forms must be in the same sense permanent, and thus originate SPECIES.[166]

Introductory Note to "On the Tendency of Varieties to Depart Indefinitely from the Original Type" [1870]. In *Natural Selection and Tropical Nature* (for full title see p. 62). (The essay to which this Note served as an introduction was published originally in the Linnean Society Papers of 1858.) Reprinted by permission of A. J. R. Wallace.

As this chapter sets forth the main features of a theory identical with that discovered by Mr. Darwin many years before but not then published, and as it has thus an historical interest, a few words of personal statement may be permissible. . . . The question of *how* changes of species could have been brought about was rarely out of my mind, but no satisfactory conclusion was reached till February 1858. At that time I was suffering from a rather severe attack of intermittent fever at Ternate in the Moluccas, and one day while lying on my bed during the cold fit, wrapped in blankets, though the thermometer was at 88°F., the problem . . . presented itself to me, and something led me to think of the "positive checks" described by Malthus in his "Essay on Population," a work I had read several years before, and which had made a deep and permanent impression on my mind. These checks—war, disease, famine and the like—must, it occurred to me, act on animals as well as on man. Then I thought of the enormously rapid multiplication of animals, causing these checks to be much more effective in them than in the case of man; and while pondering vaguely on this fact there suddenly flashed upon me the *idea* of the survival of the fittest—that the individuals removed by these checks must be on the whole inferior to those that survived. In the two hours that elapsed before my ague fit was over I had thought out almost the whole of my theory, and the same evening I sketched the draft of my paper, and in the two succeeding evenings wrote it out in full, and sent it by the next post to Mr. Darwin. Up to this time the only letters I had received from him were those printed in the second volume of his *Life and Letters* (vol. ii, pp. 95 and 108),[20] in which he speaks of its being the twentieth year since he "opened his first note-book on the question how and in what way do species and varieties differ from each other," and after referring to oceanic islands, the means of distribution of landshells, etc., added: "My work, on which I have now been at work more or less for twenty years, *will not fix or settle anything;* but I hope it will aid by giving a large collection of facts, with one definite end." The words I have italicised, and the whole tone of his letters, led me to conclude that he had arrived at no definite view as to the origin of species, and I fully anticipated that my theory would be new to him, because it seemed to me to settle a great deal. The immediate result of my paper was that Darwin was induced at once to prepare for publication his book on the *Origin of Species* in the condensed form in which it appeared, instead of waiting an indefinite number of years to complete a work on a much larger scale which he had partly written, but which in all probability would not have carried conviction to so many persons in so short a time. I feel much satisfaction in having thus aided in bringing about the publication of this celebrated book, and with the ample recognition by Darwin himself of my independent discovery of "natural selection." (See *Origin of Species,* 6th ed., introduction, p. 1, and *Life and Letters,* vol. ii, chap. iv., pp. 115-129 and 145.) [21]

From "The Limits of Natural Selection as Applied to Man" [1870]. In *Natural Selection and Tropical Nature* (for full title see p. 62). Reprinted by permission of A. J. R. Wallace.

Summary of the Argument as to the Insufficiency of Natural Selection to Account for the Development of Man

The inference I would draw . . . is, that a superior intelligence has guided the development of man in a definite direction, and for a special purpose, just as man guides the development of many animal and vegetable forms. The laws of evolution alone would, perhaps, never have produced a grain so well adapted to man's use as wheat and maize; such fruits as the seedless banana and breadfruit; or such animals as the Guernsey milch cow, or the London dray-horse. Yet these so closely resemble the unaided productions of nature, that we may well imagine a being who had mastered the laws of development of organic forms through past ages, refusing to believe that any new power had been concerned in their production, and scornfully rejecting the theory (as my theory will be rejected by many who agree with me on other points) that in these few cases a controlling intelligence had directed the action of the laws of variation, multiplication, and survival, for his own purposes. We know, however, that this has been done; and we must therefore admit the possibility that, if we are not the highest intelligences in the universe, some higher intelligence may have directed the process by which the human race was developed, by means of more subtle agencies than we are acquainted with. At the same time I must confess that this theory has the disadvantage of requiring the intervention of some distinct individual intelligence, to aid in the [204] production of what we can hardly avoid considering as the ultimate aim and outcome of all organised existence—intellectual, ever-advancing, spiritual man. It therefore implies that the great laws which govern the material universe were insufficient for his production, unless we consider (as we may fairly do) that the controlling action of such higher intelligences is a necessary part of those laws, just as the action of all surrounding organisms is one of the agencies in organic development. But even if my particular view should not be the true one, the difficulties I have put forward remain, and, I think, prove that some more general and more fundamental law underlies that of natural selection. The law of "unconscious intelligence" pervading all organic nature . . . is such a law; but to my mind it has the double disadvantage of being both unintelligible and incapable of any kind of proof. It is more probable that the true law lies too deep for us to discover it; but there seem to me to be ample indications that such a law does exist, and is probably connected with the absolute origin of life and organisation.[205]

⁕

From "The Debt of Science to Darwin" [1883]. In *Natural Selection and Tropical Nature* (for full title see p. 62). Reprinted by permission of A. J. R. Wallace.

Estimate of Darwin's Life-Work

Yet these works [Darwin's works aside from *The Origin of Species*], great as is each of them separately, and, taken altogether, amazing as the production of one man, sink into insignificance as compared with the vast body of research and of thought of which the *Origin of Species* is the brief epitome, and with which alone the name of Darwin is associated by the mass of educated men. I have here [473] endeavoured, however imperfectly, to enable non-specialists to judge of the character and extent of this work, and of the vast revolution it has effected in our conception of nature,—a revolution altogether independent of the question whether the theory of "natural selection" is or is not as important a factor in bringing about changes of animal and vegetable forms as its author maintained. Let us consider for a moment the state of mind induced by the new theory and that which preceded it. So long as men believed that every species was the immediate handiwork of the Creator, and was therefore absolutely perfect, they remained altogether blind to the meaning of the countless variations and adaptations of the parts and organs of plants and animals. They who were always repeating, parrot-like, that every organism was exactly adapted to its conditions and surroundings by an all-wise being, were apparently dulled or incapacitated by this belief from any inquiry into the inner meaning of what they saw around them, and were content to pass over whole classes of facts as inexplicable, and to ignore countless details of structure under vague notions of a "general plan," or of variety and beauty being "ends in themselves"; while he whose teachings were at first stigmatised as degrading or even atheistical, by devoting to the varied phenomena of living things the loving, patient, and reverent study of one who really had *faith* in the beauty and harmony and perfection of creation, was enabled to bring to light innumerable hidden adaptations, and to prove that the most insignificant parts of the meanest living things had a use and a purpose, were worthy of our earnest study, and fitted to excite our highest and most intelligent admiration.

That he has done this is the sufficient answer to his critics and to his few detractors. However much our knowledge of nature may advance in the future, it will certainly be by following in the pathways he has made clear for us; and for long years to come the name of Darwin will stand for the typical example of what the student of nature ought to be. And if we glance back over the whole domain of science, we shall find none to stand beside him as equals; for in him we find a patient observation and collection of facts, as in Tycho Brahe; [1] the power of using those facts in the determination of laws, as in Kepler,[2] combined with the inspirational genius of a [474] Newton, through which he was enabled to grasp fundamental principles, and so apply them as to bring order out of chaos, and illuminate the world of life as Newton illuminated the material universe. Paraphrasing the eulogistic words of a poet,[3] we may say, with perhaps a greater approximation to truth—

"Nature and Nature's laws lay hid in night;
God said, 'Let Darwin be,' and all was light." [475]

ᕫᕫ

From *Darwinism—An Exposition of the Theory of Natural Selection with Some of its Applications.* London: Macmillan and Co., 1889. Reprinted by permission of A. J. R. Wallace.

CHAPTER I—"WHAT ARE 'SPECIES,' AND WHAT IS MEANT BY THEIR 'ORIGIN' "

The Change of Opinion effected by Darwin

. . . Before Darwin's work [*The Origin of Species*] appeared, the great majority of naturalists, and almost without exception the whole literary and scientific world, held firmly to the belief that *species* were realities, and had not been derived from other species by any process accessible to us; the different species of crow and of violet [8] were believed to have been always as distinct and separate as they are now, and to have originated by some totally unknown process so far removed from ordinary reproduction that it was usually spoken of as "special creation." There was, then, no question of the origin of families, orders, and classes, because the very first step of all, the "origin of species," was believed to be an insoluble problem. But now this is all changed. The whole scientific and literary world, even the whole

---

1 Tycho Brahe (1546-1601), Danish astronomer.

2 Johannes Kepler (1571-1630), German astronomer.

3 Alexander Pope (1688-1744), whose "Epitaph Intended for Sir Isaac Newton in Westminster-Abbey" reads as Wallace has it here, with "Newton" where Wallace has put "Darwin."

educated public, accepts, as a matter of common knowledge, the origin of species from other allied species by the ordinary process of natural birth. The idea of special creation or any altogether exceptional mode of production is absolutely extinct! Yet more: this is held also to apply to many higher groups as well as to the species of a genus, and not even Mr. Darwin's severest critics venture to suggest that the primeval bird, reptile, or fish must have been "specially created." And this vast, this totally unprecedented change in public opinion has been the result of the work of one man, and was brought about in the short space of twenty years! This is the answer to those who continue to maintain that the "origin of species" is not yet discovered; that there are still doubts and difficulties; that there are divergencies of structure so great that we cannot understand how they had their beginning. We may admit all this, just as we may admit that there are enormous difficulties in the way of a complete comprehension of the origin and nature of all the parts of the solar system and of the stellar universe. But we claim for Darwin that he is the Newton of natural history, and that, just so surely as that the discovery and demonstration by Newton of the law of gravitation established order in place of chaos and laid a sure foundation for all future study of the starry heavens, so surely has Darwin, by his discovery of the law of natural selection and his demonstration of the great principle of the preservation of useful variations in the struggle for life, not only thrown a flood of light on the process of development of the whole organic world, but also established a firm foundation for all future study of nature.

In order to show the view that Darwin took of his own work, and what it was that he alone claimed to have done, the concluding passage of the introduction to the *Origin of* [9] *Species* should be carefully considered. . . .

It should be especially noted that all which is here claimed is now almost universally admitted, while the criticisms of Darwin's work refer almost exclusively to those numerous questions which, as he himself says, "will long remain obscure.". . .[10]. . . .

CHAPTER XIV—"FUNDAMENTAL PROBLEMS IN RELATION TO VARIATION AND HEREDITY"

Concluding Remarks

. . . While admitting, as Darwin always admitted, the co-operation of the fundamental laws of growth and variation, of correlation and heredity, in determining the direction of lines of variation or in the initiation of peculiar organs, we find that variation and natural selection are ever-present agencies, which take possession, as it were, of every minute change originated by these fundamental causes, check or favour their further development, or modify them in countless varied ways according to the varying needs of the organism. Whatever other causes have been at work, Natural Selection is supreme, to an extent which even Darwin himself hesitated to claim for it. The more we study it the more we are convinced of its over-powering importance, and the more confidently we claim in Darwin's own words, that it "has been the most important, but not the exclusive, means of modification." [444]

CHAPTER XV—"DARWINISM APPLIED TO MAN"

Concluding Remarks

Those who admit my interpretation of the evidence now adduced —strictly scientific evidence in its appeal to facts which are clearly what ought *not* to be on the materialistic theory—will be able to accept the spiritual nature of man, as not in any way inconsistent with the theory of evolution, but as dependent on those fundamental laws and causes which furnish the very materials for evolution to work with. They will also be relieved from the crushing mental burthen imposed upon those who—maintaining that we, in common with the [476] rest of nature, are but products of the blind eternal forces of the universe, and believing also that the time must come when the sun will lose his heat and all life on the earth necessarily cease—have to contemplate a not very distant future in which all this glorious earth—which for untold millions of years has been slowly developing forms of life and beauty to culminate at last in man—shall be as if it had never existed; who are compelled to suppose that all the slow growths of our race struggling towards a higher life, all the agony of martyrs, all the groans of victims, all the evil and misery and undeserved suffering of the ages, all the struggles for freedom, all the efforts towards justice, all the aspirations for virtue and the wellbeing of humanity, shall absolutely vanish and, "like the baseless fabric of a vision, leave not a wrack behind."

As contrasted with this hopeless and soul-deadening belief, we, who accept the existence of a spiritual world, can look upon the universe as a grand consistent whole adapted in all its parts to the development of spiritual beings capable of indefinite life and perfectibility. To us, the whole purpose, the only *raison d'être* of the world—with all its complexities of physical structure, with its grand geological progress, the slow evolution of the vegetable and animal kingdoms, and the ultimate appearance of man—was the development of the human spirit in association with the human body. From the fact that the spirit of man—the man himself—*is* so developed, we may well believe that this is the only, or at least the best, way for its development; and we may even see in what is usually termed "evil" on the earth, one of the most efficient means of its growth. For we know that the noblest faculties of man are strengthened and perfected by struggle and effort; it is by unceasing warfare against physical evils and in the midst of difficulty and danger that energy, courage, self-reliance, and industry have become the common qualities of the northern races; it is by the battle with moral evil in all its hydra-headed forms, that the still nobler qualities of justice and mercy and humanity and self-sacrifice have been steadily increasing in the world. Beings thus trained and strengthened by their surroundings, and possessing latent faculties capable of such noble development, are surely destined for a higher and more permanent existence; [477] . . . .

We thus find that the Darwinian theory, even when carried out to its extreme logical conclusion, not only does not oppose, but lends a decided support to, a belief in the spiritual nature of man. It shows us how man's body may have been developed from that of a lower animal form under the law of natural selection; but it also teaches us that we possess intellectual and moral faculties which could not have been so developed, but must have had another origin; and for this origin we can only find an adequate cause in the unseen universe of Spirit.[478]

PART THREE
OPPONENTS OF DARWINISM

Outspoken opposition to Darwinism, ranging
from the charitably critical to the wildly vi-
tuperative, developed soon after the publication of *The Origin of Species.* Three anonymously published reviews of that work were
written by Samuel Wilberforce, Bishop of Oxford, by Adam Sedgwick, distinguished British
geologist, and by Richard Owen, one of England's leading comparative anatomists. Of
Darwin's many opponents, some believed that
species did not evolve, naturally or otherwise,
but were instead "special creations" of God.
To this group belonged not only Wilberforce
and Sedgwick, but also Louis Agassiz, Swiss-
American naturalist, and John W. Dawson,
Canadian geologist. Others, like St. George
Mivart, British biologist, and Samuel Butler,
British novelist and miscellaneous writer, believed in organic evolution but pointedly rejected natural selection. Mivart argued in
support of a purposeful, internal force to
account for evolution, while Butler subscribed
to the principles of Lamarck.

Adam Sedgwick (1785-1873)

[Published anonymously.] From "Objections to Mr. Darwin's Theory of the Origin of Species." In *The Spectator,* XXXIII (March 24, 1860), 285-286.

. . . I must in the first place observe that Darwin's theory is not *inductive,*—not based on a series of acknowledged facts pointing to a general conclusion,—not a proposition evolved out of the facts, logically, and of course including them. To use an old figure, I look on the theory as a vast pyramid resting on its apex, and that apex a mathematical point. The only facts he pretends to adduce, as true elements of proof, are the *varieties* produced by domestication, or the *human artifice* of cross-breeding. We all admit the varieties, and the very wide limits of variation, among domestic animals. How very unlike are poodles and greyhounds. Yet they are of one species. And how nearly alike are many animals,—allowed to be of distinct species, on any acknowledged views of species. Hence there may have been very many blunders among naturalists, in the discrimination and enumeration of species. But this does not undermine the grand truth of nature, and the continuity of species. Again, the varieties, built upon by Mr. Darwin, are varieties of domestication and human *design*. Such varieties could have no existence in the old world. Something may be done by cross-breeding; but mules are generally sterile, or the progeny (in some rare instances) passes into one of the original crossed forms. The Author of Nature will not permit His work to be spoiled by the wanton curiosity of Man. And in a state of nature (such as that of the old world before Man came upon it) wild animals of different species do not desire to cross and unite.

Species have been constant for thousands of years; and time (so far as I see my way) though multiplied by millions and billions would never change them, so long as the conditions remained constant. Change the conditions, and the old species would disappear; and new species *might* have room to come in and flourish. But how, and by what causation? I say by *creation*. But, what do I mean by creation? I reply, the operation of a power quite beyond the powers of a pigeon-fancier, a cross-breeder, or hybridizer; a power I cannot imitate or comprehend; but in which I can believe, by a legitimate conclusion of sound reason drawn from the laws and harmonies of Nature,—proving in all around me a design and purpose, and a mutual adaptation of parts, which I *can* comprehend,—and which prove that there is exterior to, and above, the mere phenomena of Nature a great prescient and designing cause. Believing this, I have no difficulty in the repetition of new species.

But Darwin would say I am introducing a *miracle* by the supposition. In one sense I am; in another I am not. The hypothesis does not suspend or interrupt an established law of Nature. It does suppose the introduction of a new phenomenon unaccounted for by the operation of any *known* law of Nature; and it appeals to a power above established laws, and yet acting in conformity with them.

The pretended physical philosophy of modern days strips Man of all his moral attributes, or holds them of no account in the estimate of his origin and place in the created world. A cold atheistical materialism is the tendency of the so-called material philosophy of the present day. Not that I believe that Darwin is an atheist; though I cannot but regard his materialism as atheistical. I think it untrue, because opposed to the obvious course of Nature, and the very opposite of inductive truth. And I think it intensely mischievous.

Let no one say that it is held together by a *cumulative* argument. Each series of facts is laced together by a series of assumptions, and repetitions of the one false principle. You cannot make a good rope out of a string of air bubbles. . . .

I proceed now to notice the manner in which Darwin tries to fit his principles to the facts of geology.

I will take for granted that the known series of fossil-bearing rocks or deposits may be divided into the Palaeozoic, the Mesozoic, the Tertiary or Neozoic, and the Modern,[1] the Fens, Deltas, &c., &c., with the spoils of the actual flora and fauna of the world, and with the wrecks of the works of Man.

To begin then, with the Palaeozoic rocks. Surely we ought on the transmutation theory, to find near their base great deposits with *none but the lowest forms of organic life.* I know of no such deposits. . . . We have some land reptiles (batrachian), in the higher Palaeozoic periods, but not of a very low type; and the reptiles of the permian [2] groups (at the very top of the Palaeozoic rocks,) are of a high type. If all this be true, (and I think it is,) it gives but a sturdy grist for the transmutation-mill, and may soon break its cogs.

We know the complicated organic phenomena of the Mesozoic (or Oolithic [3]) period. It defies the transmutationist at every step. Oh! but the document, says Darwin, is a fragment. I will interpolate long periods to account for all the changes. I say, in reply, if you deny my conclusion grounded on positive evidence, I toss back your conclusions, derived from negative evidence—the inflated cushion on which you

---

[1] The Tertiary and Quaternary (what Sedgwick here calls "Modern") periods together form the Cenozoic era of geological time. See Glossary.
[2] The Permian is the latest period of the Paleozoic era. See Glossary.
[3] More properly, Oölitic.

try to bolster up the defects of your hypothesis. The reptile fauna of the Mesozoic period is the grandest and highest that has lived. How came they all to die off, or to degenerate? And how came the Dinosaures [sic] to disappear from the face of Nature, and leave no descendants like themselves, or of a corresponding nobility? Did they tire of the land, and become Whales, casting off their hind-legs? And, after they had lasted millions of years as whales, did they tire of the water, and leap out again as Pachydemics [sic]? I have heard of both hypotheses; and I cannot put them in words without falling into terms of mockery. This I do affirm, that if the transmutation theory were proved true in the actual world, and we could hatch rats out of the eggs of geese, it would still be difficult to account for the successive forms of organic life in the old world. They appear to me to give the lie to the theory at every turn of the pages of Dame Nature's old book.

And now for a few words upon Darwin's long inter*polated periods* of geological ages. He has an eternity of past time to draw upon; and I am willing to give him ample measure; only let him use it logically, and in some probable accordance with facts and phenomena.

I place the theory against facts viewed collectively. 1st. I see no proofs of enormous *gaps* of geological time, (I say nothing of years or centuries,) in those cases where there is a sudden change in the ancient fauna and flora. I am willing, out of the stock of past time, to lavish millions or billions upon each epoch, if thereby we can gain rational results from the operation of *true causes*. But time and "natural selection" can do nothing if there be not a vera causa working in them. . . .

2d. Towards the end of the carboniferous period,[4] there was a vast extinction of animal and vegetable life. We can, I think, account for this extinction mechanically. The old crust was broken up. The sea bottom underwent a great change. The old flora and fauna went out; a new flora and fauna appeared, in the ground now called Permian, at the base of the new red sandstone, which overlie the carboniferous. I take the fact as it *is,* and I have no difficulty. The time in which all this was brought about *may* have been very long, even upon a geological scale of time. But where do the *intervening* and connecting types exist, which are to mark the *work of natural selection?* We do not find them. Therefore the step onwards gives no true resting-place to a baseless theory; and is, in fact, a stumbling-block in its way. . . .[285]. . . .

I need hardly go on any further with these objections. But I cannot conclude without expressing my detestation of the theory, because of its unflinching materialism;—because it has deserted the inductive track, the only track that leads to physical truth;—because

---

[4] That period of the Paleozoic era immediately preceding the Permian period. See Glossary

it utterly repudiates final causes, and thereby indicates a demoralized understanding on the part of its advocates. In some rare instances it shows a wonderful credulity. Darwin seems to believe that a white bear, by being confined to the slops floating in the Polar basin, might be turned into a whale; that a Lemur might easily be turned into a bat; that a three-toed Tapir might be the great grandfather of a horse! or the progeny of a horse may (in America) have gone back to the tapir.

But any startling and (supposed) novel paradox, maintained very boldly and with something of imposing plausibility, produces, in some minds, a kind of pleasing excitement, which predisposes them in its favour; and if they are unused to careful reflection, and averse to the labour of accurate investigation, they will be likely to conclude that what is (apparently) *original,* must be a production of original *genius,* and that anything very much opposed to prevailing notions must be a grand discovery,—in short, that whatever comes from "the bottom of a well" must be the "truth" supposed to be hidden there.[286]

~~~~~~~

Richard Owen (1804-1892)

[Published anonymously.] From untitled review of Darwin's *The Origin of Species* and of nine other related works on evolution. In *The Edinburgh Review,* CXI (April, 1860), 487-532.

The scientific world has looked forward with great interest to the facts which Mr. Darwin might finally deem adequate to the support of his theory . . . , and to the course of inductive original research which might issue in throwing light on 'that mystery of mysteries.' But having now cited the chief, if not the whole, of the original observations adduced by its author in the volume now before us, our disappointment may be conceived. . . .[495] . . . .

. . . We have no sympathy whatever with Biblical objectors to creation by law, or with the sacerdotal revilers of those who would explain such law. . . . What we have here to do, is to express our views of the hypothesis as to the nature and mode of operation of the creative law, which has been promulgated by Messrs. Wallace and Darwin.

The author of the volume 'On the Origin of Species,' starts [511] from a single supernaturally created form. He does not define it; it may have been beyond his power of conception. It is, however, eminently plastic, is modified by the influence of external circumstances, and propagates such modifications by generation. Where such modified descendants find favourable conditions of existence, there they thrive; where otherwise they perish. In the first state of things, the result is so analogous to that which man brings about, in establishing a breed of domestic animals from a selected stock, that it suggested the phrase of 'Natural Selection;' and we are appealed to, or at least 'the young and rising naturalists with plastic minds,' are adjured, to believe that the reciprocal influences so defined have operated, through divergence of character and extinction, on the descendants of a common parent, so as to produce all the organic beings that live, or have ever lived, on our planet.

Now we may suppose that the primeval prototype began by producing, in the legal generative way, creatures like itself, or so slightly affected by external influences, as at first to be scarcely distinguishable from their parent. When, as the progeny multiplied and diverged, they came more and more under the influence of 'Natural Selection,' so, through countless ages of this law's operation, they finally rose to man. But, we may ask, could any of the prototype's descendants utterly escape the surrounding influences? To us such immunity, in the illimitable period during which the hypothesis of Natural Selection requires it to have operated, is inconceivable. No living being, therefore, can now manifest the mysterious primeval form to which Darwin restricts the direct creative act; and we may presume that this inevitable consequence of his hypothesis, became to him an insuperable bar to the definition of that form.

But do the facts of actual organic nature square with the Darwinian hypothesis? Are all the recognised organic forms of the present date, so differentiated, so complex, so superior to conceivable primordial simplicity of form and structure, as to testify to the effects of Natural Selection continuously operating through untold time? Unquestionably not. The most numerous living beings now on the globe are precisely those which offer such a simplicity of form and structure, as best agrees, and we take leave to affirm can only agree, with that ideal prototype from which, by any hypothesis of natural law, the series of vegetable and animal life might have diverged.

If by the patient and honest study and comparison of plants [512] and animals, under their manifold diversities of matured form, and under every step of development by which such form is attained, any idea may be gained of a hypothetical primitive organism,—if its nature is not to be left wholly to the unregulated fancies of dreamy speculation—we should say that the form and condition of life which are common, at one period of existence, to every known kind and grade of organism, would be the only conceivable form and condition of the one primordial being from which 'Natural Selection' infers that all the organisms which have ever lived on this earth have descended.

Now the form in question is the nucleated cell, having the powers of receiving nutritive matter from without, of assimilating such nutriment, and of propagating its kind by spontaneous fission. . . .[513]. . . .

. . . We find that every grade of structure, from the lowest to the highest, from the most simple to the most complex, is now in being,—a result which it is impossible to reconcile with the Darwinian hypothesis of the one and once only created primordial form, the parent of all subsequent living things. . . .[515]. . . .

It is assumed by Mr. Darwin that variations, useful in some way to each being, occur naturally in the course of thousands of generations, that such variations are reproduced in the offspring, and, if in harmony with external circumstances, may be heightened in still further modified descendants of the species. The transmission and exaggeration of a variety, step by step, in the generative series, essential to the theory of 'natural selection,' implies the fertility of the individuals constituting the several steps of the series of transmutation. But numerous instances, familiar to every zoologist, suggest an objection which seems fatal to the theory, since they show extreme peculiarities of structure and instinct in individuals that cannot transmit them, because they are doomed to perpetual sterility. . . .[524]. . . .

Such are the signs of defective information which contribute, almost at each chapter, to check our confidence in the teachings and advocacy of the hypothesis of 'Natural Selection.' But, as we have before been led to remark, most of Mr. Darwin's statements elude, by their vagueness and incompleteness, the test of Natural History facts. . . .[528]. . . .

Lasting and fruitful conclusions have, indeed, hitherto been based only on the possession of knowledge; now we are called upon to accept an hypothesis on the plea of want of knowledge. The geological record, it is averred, is so imperfect! But what human record is not? . . .

Mr. Darwin asks, 'How is it that varieties, which I have called incipient species, become ultimately good and distinct species?' To which we rejoin with the question:—Do they become good and distinct species? Is there any one instance proved by observed facts of such transmutation? We have searched the volume in vain for such. When we see the intervals that divide most species from their nearest congeners,[1] in the recent and especially the fossil series, we either doubt the fact of progressive conversion, or, as Mr. Darwin remarks in his letter to Dr. Asa Gray, one's 'imagination must fill up very wide blanks.' . . .[530]. . . .

. . . Transmutation, gradual or abrupt, is . . . mere assumption. We have no objection on any score to the change [occurring in species];

---

[1] Members of the same genus.

we have the greatest desire to know how it is brought about. Owen [2] has long stated his belief that some preordained law or secondary cause is operative in bringing about the change; but our knowledge of such law if such exists, can only be acquired on the prescribed terms. . . .[532]

~~~~~~~~~

Samuel Wilberforce (1805-1873)

[Published anonymously.] From untitled review of Darwin's *The Origin of Species*. In *The Quarterly Review*, CVIII (July, 1860), 225-264.

We think it difficult to find a theory fuller of assumptions [than Darwin's theory of natural selection]; and of assumptions not grounded upon alleged facts in nature, but which are absolutely opposed to all the facts we have been able to observe.

1. We have already shown that the variations of which we have proof under domestication have never, under the longest and most [287] continued system of selections we have known, laid the first foundation of a specific difference, but have always tended to relapse, and not to accumulated and fixed persistence.

But, 2ndly, all these variations have the essential characteristics of *monstrosity* about them; and *not one* of them has the character which Mr. Darwin repeatedly reminds us is the *only one* which nature can select, viz. of being an advantage to the selected individual in the battle for life, *i.e.* an improvement upon the normal type by raising some individual of the species not to the highest possible excellence within the species, but to some excellence above it. So far from this, every variation introduced by man is for man's advantage, not for the advantage of the animal. . . . There is not a shadow of ground for saying that man's variations ever improve the typical character of the animal as an animal; they do but by some monstrous development make it more useful to himself; and hence it is that Nature, according to her universal law with monstrosities, is ever tending to obliterate the deviation and to return to the type.

The applied argument then, from variation under domestication, fails utterly. But further, what does observation say as to the occurrence of a single instance of such favourable variation? Men have now

---

2 The reference is to the author of the review, Richard Owen, himself.

for thousands of years been conversant as hunters and other rough naturalists with animals of every class. Has any one such instance ever been discovered? We fearlessly assert not one. Variations have been found . . . but *not one* which has tended to raise the individual in the struggle of life above the typical conditions of its own species. Mr. Darwin himself allows that he finds none; . . .[238] . . .

. . . All the facts presented to us in the natural world tend to show that none of the variations produced in the fixed forms of animal life, when seen in its most plastic condition under domestication, give any promise of a true transmutation of species; first, from the difficulty of accumulating and fixing variations within the same species; secondly, from the fact that these variations, though most serviceable for man, have no tendency to improve the individual beyond the standard of his own specific type, and so to afford matter, even if they were infinitely produced, for the supposed power of natural selection on which to work; whilst all variations from the mixture of species are barred by the inexorable law of hybrid sterility. Further, the embalmed records of 3000 years show that there has been no beginning of transmutation in the species of our most familiar domesticated animals; and beyond this, that in the countless tribes of animal life around us, down to its lowest and most variable species, no one has ever been known to be developed—no new natural instinct to be formed—whilst, finally, in the vast museum of departed animal life which the strata of the earth imbed for our examination, whilst they contain far too complete a representation of the past to be set aside as a mere imperfect record, yet afford no one instance of any such change as having ever been in progress, or give us anywhere the missing links of the assumed chain, or [247] the remains which would enable now existing variations by gradual approximations, to shade off into unity.

On what then is the new theory based? We say it with unfeigned regret, in dealing with such a man as Mr. Darwin, on the merest hypothesis, supported by the most unbounded assumptions. . . .[248] . . .

. . . Place the first beginning where you will, that beginning *must* contain the apparent history of a *past*, which existed only in the mind of the Creator. If, with Mr. Darwin, to escape the difficulty of supposing the first man at his creation to possess in that framework of his body 'false marks of nourishment from his mother's womb,' with Mr. Darwin you consider him to have been an improved ape, you only carry the difficulty up from the first man to the first ape; if, with Mr. Darwin, in violation of all observation, you break the barrier between the classes of vegetable and animal life, and suppose every animal to be an 'improved' vegetable, you do but carry your difficulty with you into the vegetable world; for, how could there be seeds if there had been no plants to seed them? and if you carry up your thoughts through the vista of the Darwinian eternity up to the primaeval fungus, still the primaeval fungus must have had humus, from which to draw into its venerable vessels the nourishment of its arche-typal existence, and that humus must itself be a 'false mark' of a pre-existing vegetation. . . .[253]. . . .

Our readers will not have failed to notice that we have objected to the views with which we have been dealing solely on scientific grounds. We have done so from our fixed conviction that it is thus that the truth or falsehood of such arguments should be tried. We have no sympathy with those who object to any facts or alleged facts in nature, or to any inference logically deduced from them, because they believe them to contradict what it appears to them is taught by Revelation. We think that all such objections savour of a timidity which is really inconsistent with a firm and well-instructed faith. . . . He who is as sure as he is of his own existence that the God of Truth is at once the God of Nature and the God of Revelation, cannot believe it to be possible that His voice in either, rightly understood, can differ, or deceive His creatures. To oppose facts in the natural world because they seem to oppose Revelation, or to humour them so as to compel them to speak its voice, is, he knows, but another form of the ever-ready feebleminded dishonesty of lying for God, and trying by fraud or falsehood to do the work of the God of truth. It is with another and a nobler spirit that the true believer walks amongst the works of nature. The words graven on the everlasting rocks are the words of God, and they are graven by His hand. No more can they contradict His Word written in His book, than could the words of the old [256] covenant graven by His hand on the stony tables contradict the writing of His hand in the volume of the new dispensation. There may be to man difficulty in reconciling all the utterances of the two voices. But what of that? He has learned already that here he knows only in part, and that the day of reconciling all apparent contra-dictions between what must agree is nigh at hand. He rests his mind in perfect quietness on this assurance, and rejoices in the gift of light without a misgiving as to what it may discover. . . .

Mr. Darwin writes as a Christian, and we doubt not that he is one. We do not for a moment believe him to be one of those who retain in some corner of their hearts a secret unbelief which they dare not vent; and we therefore pray him to consider well the grounds on which we brand his speculations with the charge of such a tendency. First, then, he not obscurely declares that he applies his scheme of the action of the principle of natural selection to MAN himself, as well as to the animals around him.[257] Now, we must say at once, and openly, that such a notion is absolutely incompatible not only with single expres-sions in the word of God on that subject of natural science with which it is not immediately concerned, but, which in our judgment is of far more importance, with the whole representation of that moral and spiritual condition of man which is its proper subject-matter. Man's derived supremacy over the earth; man's power of articulate speech; man's gift of reason; man's free-will and responsibility; man's fall and man's redemption; the incarnation of the Eternal Son; the indwelling of the Eternal Spirit,—all are equally and utterly irreconcilable with the degrading notion of the brute origin of him who was created in the image of God, and redeemed by the Eternal Son assuming to himself his nature. Equally inconsistent, too, not with any passing expressions, but with the whole scheme of God's dealing with man as recorded in His word, is Mr. Darwin's daring notion of man's further development into some unknown extent of powers, and shape, and size, through natural selection acting through that long vista of ages which he casts mistily over the earth upon the most favoured individuals of his species. We care not in these pages to push the argument further. We have done enough for our purpose in thus succinctly intimating its course. . . .

Nor can we doubt, secondly, that this view, which thus contradicts the revealed relation of creation to its Creator, is equally inconsistent with the fulness of His glory. It is, in truth, an ingenious theory for diffusing throughout creation the working and so the personality of the Creator. And thus, however unconsciously to him who holds them, such views really tend inevitably to banish from the mind most of the peculiar attributes of the Almighty.

How, asks Mr. Darwin, can we possibly account for the manifest plan, order, and arrangement which pervade creation, except we allow to it this self-developing power through modified descent? . . .[258] . . . .

How can we account for all this? By the simplest and yet the most comprehensive answer. By declaring the stupendous fact that all creation is the transcript in matter of ideas eternally existing in the mind of the Most High—that order in the utmost perfectness of its relation pervades His works, because it exists as in its centre and highest fountain-head in Him the Lord of all. Here is the true account of the fact which has so utterly misled shallow observers, that Man himself, the Prince and Head of this creation, passes in the earlier stages of his being through phases of existence closely analogous, so far as his earthly tabernacle is concerned, to those in which the lower animals ever remain. At that point of being the development of the protozoa is arrested. Through it the embryo of their chief passes to the perfection of his earthly frame. But the types of those lower forms of being must be found in the animals which never advance beyond them—not in man for whom they are but the foundation for an after-development; whilst he too, Creation's crown and perfection, thus bears witness in his own frame to the law of order which pervades the universe. . . . [259] . . . .

. . . We trust that he [Darwin] is mistaken in believing that he may count Sir C. Lyell as one of his converts. We know indeed the temptations which he can bring to bear upon his geological brother.

The Lyellian hypothesis, itself not free from some of Mr. Darwin's faults, stands eminently in need for its own support of some such new scheme of physical life as that propounded here. Yet no man has been more distinct and more logical in the denial of the transmutation of species than Sir C. Lyell, and that not in the infancy of his scientific life, but in its full vigour and maturity. . . .[263]. . . .

He [Lyell] shows the fallacy of Lamarck's reasoning, and by anticipation confutes the whole theory of Mr. Darwin, when gathering clearly up into a few heads the recapitulation of the whole argument in favour of the reality of species in nature. . . .

We trust that Sir C. Lyell abides still by these truly philosophical principles; and that with his help and with that of his brethren this flimsy speculation may be as completely put down as was what in spite of all denials we must venture to call its twin though less-instructed brother, the 'Vestiges of Creation.' [1] In so doing they will assuredly provide for the strength and continually growing progress of British science. . . .[264]

Louis Agassiz (1807-1873)

From *Contributions to the Natural History of the United States of America*. Volume III. Boston: Little, Brown & Co., 1860.

Darwin, in his recent work on the "Origin of Species," has . . . done much to shake the belief in the real existence of species; but the views he advocates are entirely at variance with those I have attempted to establish. For many years past I have lost no opportunity to urge the idea, that while species have no material existence, they yet exist as categories of thought, in the same way as genera, families, orders, classes, and branches of the animal kingdom. Darwin's fundamental idea, on the contrary, is, that species, genera, families, orders, classes, and any other kind of more or less comprehensive divisions among animals, do not exist at all, and are altogether artificial, differing from one another only in degree, all having originated from a successive differentiation of a primordial organic form, undergoing successively such changes as would at first produce a variety of species; then genera, as the difference became more extensive and deeper; then families, as the gap widened still farther between the groups; until, in the end, all that diversity was produced which has existed or which now exists. Far from agreeing with these views, I have, on the contrary, taken the

---

[1] See p. 45, footnote 2.

ground that all the natural divisions in the animal kingdom are primarily distinct, founded upon different categories of characters, and that all exist in the same way, that is, as categories of thought embodied in individual living forms. . . .[88]. . . .

. . . Had Darwin or his followers furnished a single fact to show that individuals change, in the course of time, in such a manner as to produce, at last, species different from those known before, the state of the case might be different. But it stands recorded now as before, that the animals known to the [89] ancients are still in existence exhibiting to this day the characters they exhibited of old. The geological record, even with all its imperfections exaggerated to distortion, tells now, what it has told from the beginning, that the supposed intermediate forms between the species of different geological periods are imaginary beings, called up merely in support of a fanciful theory. The origin of all the diversity among living beings remains a mystery, as totally unexplained as if the book of Darwin had never been written; for no theory, unsupported by fact, however plausible it may appear, can be admitted in science.[90]. . . .

. . . [Darwin] has lost sight of the most striking of the features, and the one which pervades the whole, namely, that there runs throughout nature unmistakable evidence of thought, corresponding to the mental operations of our own mind, and therefore intelligible to us as thinking beings, and unaccountable on any other basis than that they owe their existence to the working of intelligence; and no theory that overlooks this element can be true to nature. . . .[92]. . . . Until . . . it can be shown that any one species has the ability to delegate . . . specified peculiarities and relations to any other species or set of species, it is not logical to assume that such a power is inherent in any animal, or that it constitutes part of its nature. We must look to the original power that imparted life to the first being for the origin of all other beings, however mysterious and inaccessible the modes by which all this diversity has been produced, may remain for us. A plausible explanation is no explanation at all, if it does not cover the whole ground.[1] [94]. . . .

---

[1] All the attempts to explain the origin of species may be brought under two categories: some naturalists admitting that all organized beings are created (that is to say, endowed from the beginning of their existence with all their characteristics), while others assume that they arise spontaneously. This classification of the different theories of the origin of species may appear objectionable to the supporters of the transmutation theory; but I can perceive no essential difference between their views and the old idea that animals may have arisen spontaneously. They differ only in the modes by which the spontaneous appearance is assumed to be effected. . . . Unless Darwin and his followers succeed in showing that the struggle for life tends to something beyond favoring the existence of certain individuals over that of other individuals, they will soon find that they are following a shadow . . . [Agassiz' note.]

From *Methods of Study in Natural History.*
Boston: Ticknor and Fields, 1863.

PREFACE:

. . . Although the direct intention of these pages has been, as
their title indicates, to give some general hints to young students as
to the methods by which scientific truth has been reached, . . . yet
I have also wished to avail myself of this opportunity to enter my
earnest protest against the transmutation theory, revived of late with
so much ability, and so generally received. It is my belief that naturalists are chasing a phantom, in their search after some material grada-
tion among created beings, by which the whole Animal Kingdom may
have been derived by successive development from a [iii] single germ,
or from a few germs. It would seem, from the frequency with which
this notion is revived,—ever returning upon us with hydra-headed
tenacity of life, and presenting itself under a new form as soon as the
preceding one has been exploded and set aside,—that it has a certain
fascination for the human mind. This arises, perhaps, from the desire
to explain the secret of our own existence; to have some simple and
easy solution of the fact that we live.

I confess that there seems to me to be a repulsive poverty in this
material explanation, that is contradicted by the intellectual grandeur
of the universe; the resources of the Deity cannot be so meagre, that,
in order to create a human being endowed with reason, he must
change a monkey into a man. . . .[iv] . . .

CHAPTER X—"SPECIES AND BREEDS"

There is one question respecting Species that gives rise to very
earnest discussions in our day, not only among naturalists, but among
all thinking people. How far are they permanent, and how far
mutable? . . . . [140] . . . .

The domesticated animals with their numerous breeds are constantly adduced as evidence of the changes which animals may undergo,
and as furnishing hints respecting the way in which the diversity now
observed among animals may have been produced. It is my conviction
that such inferences are in no way sustained by the facts of the case,
and that, however striking the differences may be between the breeds
of our domesticated animals, as compared with the wild Species of
the same Genus, they are of a peculiar character, entirely distinct from
the features prevailing among the latter, and altogether incidental to
the circumstances under which they appear. By this I do not mean
the natural action of physical conditions, but the more or less intelligent direction of the circumstances under which they live. The
inference drawn from the varieties introduced among animals in a

state of domestication, with reference to the origin of Species, is usually this: that what the farmer does on a small scale Nature may do on a large one. It is true that man has been able to produce certain changes in the animals under his care, and that these changes have resulted in a variety of breeds. But in doing this, he has, in my estimation, in [141] no way altered the character of the Species, but only developed its pliability under the will of man, that is, under a power similar in its nature and mode of action to that power to which animals owe their very existence. . . .[142] . . .

. . . All the variability among domesticated Species is due to the fostering care, or, in its more extravagant freaks, to the fancies of man; and it has never been observed in the wild Species, where, on the contrary, everything shows the closest adherence to the distinct, well-defined, invariable limits of the Species. It surely does not follow, that, because the Chinese can, under abnormal conditions, produce a variety of fantastic shapes in the Golden Carp, therefore [145] water, or the physical conditions established in the water, can create a Fish, any more than it follows, that, because they can dwarf a tree, or alter its aspect, by stunting its growth in one direction, and forcing it in another, therefore the earth, or the physical conditions connected with their growth, can create a Pine, an Oak, a Birch, or a Maple.

I confess that, in all the arguments derived from the phenomena of domestication, to prove that animals owe their origin and diversity to the natural action of the conditions under which they live, the conclusion does not seem to me to follow from the premises. And the fact that the domesticated animals of all the races of men, equally with the white race, vary among themselves in the same way, and differ in the same way from the wild Species, makes it still more evident, that domesticated varieties do not explain the origin of Species, except, as I have said, by showing, that the intelligent will of man can produce effects which physical causes have never been known to produce, and that we must, therefore, look to some cause outside of Nature, corresponding in kind to the intelligence of man, though so different in degree, for all the phenomena connected with the existence of animals in their wild state.

So far from attributing these original differences [146] among animals to natural influences, it would seem, that, while a certain freedom of development is left, within the limits of which man can exercise his intelligence and his ingenuity, not even this superficial influence is allowed to physical conditions unaided by some guiding power, since, in their normal state, the wild Species remain, so far as we have been able to discover, entirely unchanged,—maintained, it is true, in their integrity by the circumstances established for their support, but never altered by them. Nature holds inviolable the stamp that God has set upon his creatures; and if man is able to influence their organization in some slight degree, it is because the Creator has given to his relations with the animals he has intended for his companions the same plasticity which he has allowed to every other side of his life, in virtue of which he may in some sort mould and shape it to his own ends, and be held responsible also for its results.

The common sense of a civilized community has already pointed out the true distinction, in applying another word to the discrimination of the different kinds of domesticated animals. They are called Breeds, and Breeds among animals are the work of man: Species were created by God.[147]

࿙࿙࿙

stop

St. George Mivart (1827-1900)

> From "The Descent of Man" [1871]. In *Essays and Criticisms*. Volume II. Boston: Little, Brown & Co., 1892. (Published originally as a review of Darwin's *The Descent of Man* in *The Quarterly Review*, CXXXI (July, 1871), 47-90.)

In Mr. Darwin's last work we possess at length a complete and thorough exposition of his matured views. He gives us the results of the patient labour of many years' unremitting investigation and of the application of a powerful and acute intellect, combined with an extraordinary active imagination, to an unequalled collection of most varied, interesting, and important biological data. In his earlier writings a certain reticence veiled, though it did not hide, his ultimate conclusions as to the origin of our own species; but now all possibility of misunderstanding or of a repetition of former disclaimers on the part of any disciple is at an end, and the entire and naked truth as to the logical consequences of Darwinism is displayed with a frankness which we had a right to expect from the distinguished author. What was but obscurely hinted in the *Origin of Species* is here fully and fairly stated in all its bearings and without disguise. Mr. Darwin has, in fact, 'crowned the edifice,' and the long looked for and anxiously awaited detailed statement of his views as to the human race is now unreservedly put before us.

We rise from the careful perusal of this book with mingled feelings of admiration and disappointment. The author's style is clear and attractive—clearer than in his earlier works—and his desire to avoid every kind of conscious misrepresentation is as conspicuous as ever. The [1] number of interesting facts brought forward is as surprising as is the ingenuity often displayed in his manipulation of them. Under these circumstances it is a most painful task to have to point out grave defects and serious shortcomings. . . .[2]. . . .

We may now sum up our judgment of Mr. Darwin's work on the *Descent of Man*—of its execution and tendency, of what it fails to accomplish and of what it has successfully attained.

Although the style of the work is, as we have said, fascinating, nevertheless we think that the author is somewhat encumbered with the multitude of his facts, which at times he seems hardly able to group and handle so effectively as might be expected from his special talent. Nor does he [55] appear to have maturely reflected over the data he has so industriously collected. Moreover, we are surprised to find so accurate an observer receiving as facts many statements of a very questionable nature, as we have already pointed out, and frequently on second-hand authority. The reasoning also is inconclusive, the author having allowed himself constantly to be carried away by the warmth and fertility of his imagination. In fact, Mr. Darwin's power of reasoning seems to be in an inverse ratio to his power of observation. He now strangely exaggerates the action of 'sexual selection,' as previously he exaggerated the effects of the 'survival of the fittest.' On the whole, we are convinced that by the present work the cause of 'natural selection' has been rather injured than promoted; and we confess to a feeling of surprise that the case put before us is not stronger, since we had anticipated the production of far more telling and significant details from Mr. Darwin's biological treasure-house.

A great part of the work may be dismissed as beside the point—as a mere elaborate and profuse statement of the obvious fact, which no one denies, that man is an animal, and has all the essential properties of a highly organised one. Along with this truth, however, we find the assumption that he is *no more* than an animal—an assumption which is necessarily implied in Mr. Darwin's distinct assertion that there is no difference of *kind,* but merely of *degree,* between man's mental faculties and those of brutes.

We have endeavoured to show that this is distinctly untrue. We maintain that while there is no need to abandon the received position that man is truly an animal, he is yet the only rational one known to us, and that his rationality constitutes a fundamental distinction—one of *kind* and not of *degree.* The estimate we have formed of man's position differs therefore most widely from that of Mr. Darwin. . . . [56] . . . .

If then we are right in our confident assertion that man's mental faculties are different *in kind* from those of brutes, and if he is, as we maintain, the only rational animal; then is man, as a whole, to be spoken of by preference from the point of view of his animality, or from the point of view of his rationality? Surely from the latter, and if so, we must consider not structure, but action. . . .[57] . . . .

We seem . . . to have Mr. Darwin on our side when we affirm that animals possessed of mental faculties distinct in kind, should be placed in a kingdom apart. And man possesses such a distinction.

Is this, however, all that can be said for the dignity of his position? Is he merely one division of the visible universe co-ordinate with the animal, vegetable, and mineral kingdoms?

It would be so if he were intelligent and no more. If he could observe the facts of his own existence, investigate the co-existences and successions of phenomena, but all the time remain, like the other parts of the visible universe, a mere floating unit in the stream of time, incapable of one act of free self-determination or one voluntary moral aspiration after an ideal of absolute goodness. This, however, is far [58] from being the case. Man is not merely an intellectual animal, but he is also a free moral agent, and, as such—and with the infinite future such freedom opens out before him—differs from all the rest of the visible universe by a distinction so profound that none of those which separate other visible beings is comparable with it. The gulf which lies between his being as a whole, and that of the highest brute, marks off vastly more than a mere kingdom of material beings; and man, so considered, differs far more from an elephant or a gorilla than do these from the dust of the earth on which they tread.

Thus, then, in our judgment the author of the *Descent of Man* has utterly failed in the only part of his work which is really important. Mr. Darwin's errors are mainly due to a radically false metaphysical system in which he seems (like so many other physicists) to have become entangled. Without a sound philosophical basis, however, no satisfactory scientific superstructure can ever be reared; and if Mr. Darwin's failure should lead to an increase of philosophic culture on the part of physicists, we may therein find some consolation for the injurious effects which his work is likely to produce on too many of our half-educated classes. We sincerely trust Mr. Darwin may yet live to furnish us with another work, which, while enriching physical science, shall not, with needless opposition, set at naught the first principles of both philosophy and religion.[59]

From *Lessons from Nature, as Manifested in Mind and Matter.* London: John Murray, 1876.

CHAPTER X—"SEXUAL SELECTION"

The hypothesis of "natural selection" having been found by its author unequal for the task he had assigned it, that of serving as the

explanation of specific origin, he subsequently brought forward to its
aid a subordinate hypothesis, which he termed *"sexual selection."* . . .
[302] . . .

. . . Certainly a theory which requires so many hypothetical props
can hardly be deemed [330] itself to have a very secure foundation. In
fact, reviewing what has been said in preceding chapters, I am confident in the belief, and I think it can be fully proved:—

1. That it is evident, on strictly scientific grounds, that Mr. Darwin's hypothesis, sexual selection (the action of which he now exaggerates as he formerly exaggerated that of natural selection, according
to his own present admission), cannot be maintained, and refutes
itself.

2. That the opposition to Mr. Darwin's hypothesis of sexual selection will be (like that to natural selection has been) due to this
exaggeration, i.e., to the representation of it as a main cause instead of
a merely subordinate aid.

3. That Mr. Darwin utterly misses the point concerning the real
difficulty as to man's origin through evolution, and consequently does
not even tend, in the faintest degree, to surmount the moral barrier
separating man from brutes.

I am also persuaded that the failure of Mr. Darwin and his
coadjutors in their attempt to establish a mechanical explanation of
the phenomena of the living world amounts almost to a demonstration
of the impossibility of any such explanation, and therefore that essentially distinct vital powers and principles really exist in nature.

Such powers may, I believe, be made evident to every unprejudiced mind who studies the world of men, of animals, and of
plants—the world of Biology. . . .[331]

〰〰〰

John W. Dawson (1820–1899)

From *The Story of the Earth and Man.* New
York: Harper & Brothers, 1873.

CHAPTERS XIV-XV—"PRIMITIVE MAN. CONSIDERED WITH REFERENCE
TO MODERN THEORIES AS TO HIS ORIGIN"

. . . [Evolutionism] reduces the position of man, who becomes a
descendant of inferior animals, and a mere term in a series whose end
is unknown. It removes from the study of nature the ideas of final

cause and purpose; and the evolutionist, instead of regarding the
world as a work of consummate plan, skill, and adjustment, approaches
nature as he would a chaos of fallen rocks, which may present forms
of castles and grotesque profiles of men and animals, but they are all
fortuitous and without significance. It obliterates the fine perception
of differences from the mind of the naturalist, and resolves all the
complicated relations of living things into some simple idea of descent
with modification. . . .[318]. . . .

. . . Two great leading alternatives are presented to us. Either
man is an independent product of the will of a Higher Intelligence,
acting directly or through the laws and materials of his own institution
and production, or he has been produced by an unconscious evolution
from lower things. It is true that many evolutionists, either unwilling
to offend, or not perceiving the logical consequences of their own
hypothesis, endeavour to steer a middle course, and to maintain that
the Creator has proceeded by way of evolution. But the bare, hard
logic of Spencer,[1] the greatest English authority on evolution, leaves
no place for this compromise, and shows that the theory, carried out
to its legitimate consequences, excludes the knowledge of a Creator
and the possibility of His work. We have, therefore, to choose between
evolution and creation; bearing in mind, however, that there may be
a place [321] in nature for evolution, properly limited, as well as for
other things, and that the idea of creation by no means excludes law
and second causes. . . .

. . . As evolutionists, we are required to assume certain forces, or
materials, or both, with which evolution shall begin. Darwin, in his
Origin of Species, went so far as to assume the existence of a few of
the simpler types of animals; but this view, of course, was only a
temporary resting-place for his theory. Others assume a primitive
protoplasm, or [322] physical basis of life, and arbitrarily assigning to
this substance properties now divided between organised and unorganised, and between dead and living matter, find no difficulty in de-
ducing all plants and animals from it. Still, even this cannot have been
the ultimate material. It must have been evolved from something. We
are thus brought back to certain molecules of star-dust, or certain con-
flicting forces, which must have had self-existence, and must have
potentially included all subsequent creatures. Otherwise, if with Spencer we hold that God is "unknowable," and creation "unthinkable,"
we are left suspended on nothing over a bottomless void, and must
adopt as the initial proposition of our philosophy, that all things were
made out of nothing, and by nothing; unless we prefer to doubt
whether anything exists, and to push the doctrine of relativity to the

---

[1] Herbert Spencer (1820-1903), English author and philosopher. See pp. 103-107,
108 ff.

unscientific extreme of believing that we can study the relations of things non-existent or unknown. So we must allow the evolutionist some small capital to start with; observing, however, that self-existent matter in a state of endless evolution is something of which we cannot possibly have any definite conception. . . .[323]. . . .

The reader will . . . readily perceive that the simplicity and completeness of the evolutionist theory entirely disappear when we consider the unproved assumptions on which it is based, and its failure to connect with each other some of the most important facts in nature: that, in short, it is not in any true sense a philosophy, but merely an arbitrary arrangement of facts in accordance with a number of unproved hypotheses. Such philosophies, "falsely so called," [329] have existed ever since man began to reason on nature, and this last of them is one of the weakest and most pernicious of the whole. . . . [330]. . . .

. . . [Darwin] has . . . in the "Origin of Species" and "Descent of Man," attempted merely to fill one of the breaks in the evolutionary series, that between distinct species, leaving us to receive all the rest on mere [338] faith. Even in respect to the question of species, in all the long chain between the Ascidian and the man, he has not certainly established one link; and in the very last change, that from the ape-like ancestor, he equally fails to satisfy us as to matters so trivial as the loss of the hair, which, on the hypothesis, clothed the pre-human back, and on matters so weighty as the dawn of human reason and conscience.

We thus see that evolution as an hypothesis has no basis in experience or in scientific fact, and that its imagined series of transmutations has breaks which cannot be filled. We have now to consider how it stands with the belief that man has been created by a higher power. Against this supposition the evolutionists try to create a prejudice in two ways. First, they maintain with Herbert Spencer that the hypothesis of creation is inconceivable, or, as they say, "unthinkable;" an assertion which, when examined, proves to mean only that we do not know perfectly the details of such an operation, an objection equally fatal to the origin either of matter or life, on the hypothesis of evolution. Secondly, they always refer to creation as if it must be a special miracle, in the sense of a contravention of or departure from ordinary natural laws; but this is an assumption utterly without proof, since creation may be as much according to law as evolution, though in either case the precise laws involved may be very imperfectly known. . . .[339]. . . .

What, then, is the actual statement of the theory of creation as it may be held by a modern man of science? Simply this; that all things have been produced by the Supreme Creative Will, acting either directly or through the agency of the forces and materials of His own production.[340]

This theory does not necessarily affirm that creation is miraculous, in the sense of being contrary to or subversive of law; law and order are as applicable to creation as to any other process. It does not contradict the idea of successive creations. There is no necessity that the process should be instantaneous and without progression. It does not imply that all kinds of creation are alike. There may be higher and lower kinds. It does not exclude the idea of similarity or dissimilarity of plan and function as to the products of creation. Distinct products of creation may be either similar to each other in different degrees, or dissimilar. It does not even exclude evolution or derivation to a certain extent: anything once created may, if sufficiently flexible and elastic, be evolved or involved in various ways. Indeed, creation and derivation may, rightly understood, be complementary to each other. Created things, unless absolutely unchangeable, must be more or less modified by influences from within and from without, and derivation or evolution may account for certain subordinate changes of things already made. Man, for example, may be a product of creation, yet his creation may have been in perfect harmony with those laws of procedure which the Creator has set for His own operations. He may have been preceded by other creations of things more or less similar or dissimilar. He may have been created by the same processes with some or all of these, or by different means. His body may have been created in one way, his soul in another. He [341] may, nay, in all probability would be, part of a plan of which some parts would approach very near to him in structure or functions. After his creation, spontaneous culture and outward circumstances may have moulded him into varieties, and given him many different kinds of speech and of habits. These points are so obvious to common sense that it would be quite unnecessary to insist on them, were they not habitually overlooked or misstated by evolutionists. . . .[342]. . . .

. . . Evolutionists may still be theists. We have already seen that the doctrine, as carried out to its logical consequences, excludes creation and theism. It may, however, be shown that even in its more modified forms, and when held by men who maintain that they are not atheists, it is practically atheistic, because excluding the idea of plan and design, and resolving all things into the action of unintelligent forces. It is necessary to observe this, because it is the half-way evolutionism which professes to have a Creator somewhere behind it, that is most popular; though it is, if possible, more unphilosophical than that which professes to set out from absolute and eternal nonentity, or from self-existent star-dust containing all the possibilities of the universe.

Absolute atheists recognise in Darwinism, for example, a philosophy which reduces all things to a "gradual summation of innumerable minute and accidental material operations," and in this they are more logical than those who seek to reconcile evolution with design. . . . [348] . . .

. . . The evolutionist picture wants some of the fairest lineaments of humanity, and cheats us with a semblance of man without the reality. Shave and paint your ape as you may, clothe him and set him up upon his feet, still he fails greatly of the "human form divine;" and so it is with him morally and spiritually as well. We have seen that he wants the instinct of immortality, the love of God, the mental and spiritual power of exercising dominion over the earth. The very agency by which he is evolved is of itself subversive of all these higher properties. The struggle for existence is essentially selfish, and therefore degrading. Even in the lower animals, it is a false assumption that its tendency is to elevate; for animals when driven to the utmost verge of struggle for life, become depauperated and degraded. The dog which spends its life in snarling contention with its fellow-curs for insufficient food, will not be a noble [395] specimen of its race. God does not so treat His creatures. There is far more truth to nature in the doctrine which represents him as listening to the young ravens when they cry for food. But as applied to man, the theory of the struggle for existence and survival of the fittest, though the most popular phase of evolutionism at present, is nothing less than the basest and most horrible of superstitions. It makes man not merely carnal, but devilish. It takes his lowest appetites and propensities, and makes them his God and creator. His higher sentiments and aspirations, his self-denying philanthropy, his enthusiasm for the good and true, all the struggles and sufferings of heroes and martyrs, not to speak of that self-sacrifice which is the foundation of Christianity, are in the view of the evolutionist mere loss and waste, failure in the struggle for life. What does he give us in exchange? An endless pedigree of bestial ancestors, without one gleam of high or holy tradition to enliven the procession; and for the future, the prospect that the poor mass of protoplasm which constitutes the sum of our being, and which is the sole gain of an indefinite struggle in the past, must soon be resolved again into inferior animals or dead matter. That men of thought and culture should advocate such a philosophy, argues either a strange mental hallucination, or that the higher spiritual nature has been wholly quenched within them. It is one of the saddest of many sad spectacles that our age presents. . . . [396]. . . .

Samuel Butler (1835-1902)

From *Evolution, Old and New; or, the Theories of Buffon, Dr. Erasmus Darwin, and Lamarck, as Compared with that of Mr. Charles Darwin.* London: Hardwicke and Bogue, 1879.

CHAPTER XX—"NATURAL SELECTION CONSIDERED AS A MEANS OF MODIFICATION. THE CONFUSION WHICH THIS EXPRESSION OCCASIONS"

So little is it generally understood that "evolution" and what is called "Darwinism" convey indeed the same main conclusion, but that this conclusion has been reached by two distinct roads, one of which is impregnable, while the other has already fallen into the hands of the enemy, that in the last November number of the 'Nineteenth Century,' Professor Tyndall,[1] while referring to descent with modification or evolution, speaks of it as though it were one and inseparable from Mr. Darwin's theory that it has come about mainly by means of natural selection. . . .[360]. . . .

CHAPTER XXII—"THE CASE OF THE MADEIRA BEETLES AS ILLUSTRATING THE DIFFERENCE BETWEEN THE EVOLUTION OF LAMARCK AND OF MR. CHARLES DARWIN—CONCLUSION"

The question—Evolution or Direct Creation of all species?—has been settled in favour of Evolution. A hardly less interesting and important battle has now to be fought over the question whether we are to accept the evolution of the founders of the theory—with the adjuncts hinted at by Dr. Darwin [2] and Mr. Matthew,[3] and insisted on, so far as I can gather, by Professor Hering [4] and myself—or the evolution of Mr. Darwin, which denies the purposiveness or teleology inherent in evolution as first propounded. I am assured that such of my readers as I can persuade to prefer the old evolution to the new will have but little reason to regret their preference. . . .[382]. . . .

---

[1] John Tyndall (1820-1893), English physicist.

[2] That is, Erasmus Darwin. See p. 45, footnote 3.

[3] One Patrick Matthew (dates obscure, but a contemporary of Darwin), a Scottish botanist who anticipated Darwin's theory of natural selection in his work, *On Naval Timber and Arboriculture*, published in 1831.

[4] Ewald Hering (1834-1918), German physiologist and psychologist, to whom Butler was indebted for some of his views on evolution.

From *Unconscious Memory*. New ed. London: A. C. Fifield, 1910. (Published originally in 1880.)

CHAPTER XIII—"CONCLUSION"

. . . I may predict with some certainty that before long we shall find the original Darwinism of Dr. Erasmus Darwin . . . generally accepted instead of the neo-Darwinism of to-day, and that the variations whose accumulation results in species will be recognised as due to the wants and endeavours of the living forms in which they appear, instead of being ascribed to chance, or, in other words, to unknown causes, as by Mr. Charles Darwin's system. We shall have some idyllic young naturalist bringing up Dr. Erasmus Darwin's note on *Trapa natans,* and Lamarck's kindred passage on the descent of *Ranunculus hederaceus* from *Ranunculus aquatilis* as fresh discoveries, and be told, with much happy simplicity, that those animals and plants which have felt the need of such or such a structure have developed it, while those which have not wanted it have gone without it. Thus, it will be declared, every leaf we see around us, every structure of the minutest insect, will bear witness to the truth of the "great guess" of the greatest of naturalists [1] concerning the memory of living matter.

I dare say the public will not object to this, and am very sure that none of the admirers of Mr. Charles Darwin or Mr. Wallace will protest against it; but it may be as well to point out that this was not the view of the matter taken by Mr. Wallace in 1858 when he and Mr. Darwin first came forward as preachers of natural selection. . . . [181] . . . .

. . . Mr. Wallace, after years of reflection, still adhered to this view [i.e., the view expressed in 1858] . . . ; nor do any of his more recent works show that he has modified his opinion. It should be noted that Mr. Wallace does not call his work [2] "Contributions to the Theory of Evolution," but to that of "Natural Selection."

Mr. Darwin, with characteristic caution, only commits himself to saying that Mr. Wallace has arrived at *almost* (italics mine) the same general conclusions as he, Mr. Darwin, has done; but he still, as in 1859, declares that it would be "a serious error to suppose that the greater number of instincts have been acquired by habit in one [182] generation, and then transmitted by inheritance to succeeding generations," and he still comprehensively condemns the "well-known doctrine of inherited habit, as advanced by Lamarck."

---

[1] Apparently a reference to Lamarck. Butler's contention, as indicated by the title of his work, was that the progressive evolution of organisms was carried out by the operation of their "unconscious memory."

[2] Published originally in 1870.

As for the statement in the passage quoted from Mr. Wallace, to the effect that Lamarck's hypothesis "has been repeatedly and easily refuted by all writers on the subject of varieties and species," it is a very surprising one. I have searched Evolution literature in vain for any refutation of the Erasmus Darwinian system (for this is what Lamarck's hypothesis really is) which need make the defenders of that system at all uneasy. The best attempt at any answer to Erasmus Darwin that has yet been made is "Paley's Natural Theology," [3] which was throughout obviously written to meet Buffon [4] and the "Zoonomia." [5] It is the manner of theologians to say that such and such an objection "has been refuted over and over again," without at the same time telling us when and where; it is to be regretted that Mr. Wallace has here taken a leaf out of the theologians' book. His statement is one which will not pass muster with those whom public opinion is sure in the end to follow.

Did Mr. Herbert Spencer, for example, "repeatedly and easily refute" Lamarck's hypothesis in his brilliant attack in the *Leader,* March 20, 1852? On the contrary, that article is expressly directed against those "who cavalierly reject the hypothesis of Lamarck and his followers." This article was written six years before the words last quoted from Mr. Wallace; how absolutely, however, does the word "cavalierly" apply to them! . . .[183]. . . .

Professor Huxley in his article on Evolution [in the *Encyclopædia Britannica,* 9th ed.] is no less cavalier than Mr. Wallace. He writes:—

"Lamarck introduced the conception of the action of an animal on itself as a factor in producing modification."

[Lamarck did nothing of the kind. It was Buffon and Dr. Darwin who introduced this, but more especially Dr. Darwin.] [6]

"But *a little consideration showed*" (italics mine) "that though Lamarck had seized what, as far as it goes, is a true cause of modification, it is a cause the actual effects of which are wholly inadequate to account for any considerable modification in animals, and which can have no influence whatever in the vegetable world, &c." [184]

I should be very glad to come across some of the "little consideration" which will show this. I have searched for it far and wide, and have never been able to find it.

I think Professor Huxley has been exercising some of his ineradicable tendency to try to make things clear in the article on Evolu-

---

[3] William Paley (1743-1805), English theologian, whose *Natural Theology: or, Evidences of the Existence and Attributes of the Deity, Collected from the Appearances of Nature* was published in 1802.

[4] Georges Louis Leclerc, Comte de Buffon (1707-1788), French naturalist.

[5] Erasmus Darwin's work published in 1794-96.

[6] Butler's editorial comment.

tion, already so often quoted from. We find him . . . pooh-poohing Lamarck, yet on the next page he says, "How far 'natural selection' suffices for the production of species remains to be seen." And this when "natural selection" was already so nearly of age! Why, to those who know how to read between a philosopher's lines, the sentence comes to very nearly the same as a declaration that the writer has no great opinion of "natural selection." Professor Huxley continues, "Few can doubt that, if not the whole cause, it is a very important factor in that operation." A philosopher's words should be weighed carefully, and when Professor Huxley says "few can doubt," we must remember that he may be including himself among the few whom he considers to have the power of doubting on this matter. He does not say "few will," but "few can" doubt, as though it were only the enlightened who would have the power of doing so. Certainly "nature,"—for this is what "natural selection" comes to,—is rather an important factor in the operation, but we do not gain much by being told so. If, however, Professor Huxley neither believes in the origin of species, through sense of need on the part of animals themselves, nor yet in "natural selection," we should be glad to know what he does believe in.

The battle is one of greater importance than appears at first sight. It is a battle between teleology and non-teleology, between the purposiveness and the non-purposiveness of the organs in animal and vegetable bodies. According to Erasmus Darwin, Lamarck, and Paley, organs are purposive; according to Mr. Darwin and his followers, they are not purposive. But the main arguments against the system of Dr. Erasmus Darwin are [185] arguments which, so far as they have any weight, tell against evolution generally. Now that these have been disposed of, and the prejudice against evolution has been overcome, it will be seen that there is nothing to be said against the system of Dr. Darwin and Lamarck which does not tell with far greater force against that of Mr. Charles Darwin and Mr. Wallace.[186]

PART FOUR

NEW DEVELOPMENTS: DARWINISM MODIFIED

1. "Neo-Darwinism" versus "Neo-Lamarckism"

Anti-evolutionism and anti-Darwinism continued to manifest themselves until the end of the nineteenth century, though with less and less force. By the turn of the century, those who assumed the label of "true Darwinians" had formed two rival camps. The "Neo-Darwinians," with the German biologist August Weismann as one of their chief spokesmen, accepted the principle of natural selection without qualification. The "Neo-Lamarckians," who included the British philosopher Herbert Spencer and the German biologist Ernst Haeckel, one of Darwin's earliest European defenders, maintained that Darwin himself had accepted certain fundamental Lamarckian concepts, such as that of the transmission of acquired characteristics, which they also accepted. In 1893, the quarrel among the Darwinians found particularly concise expression in a series of articles in *The Contemporary Review* by Weismann, Spencer, and George Romanes, a British naturalist and a prolific writer on evolution.

Herbert Spencer (1820-1903)

From "The Inadequacy of 'Natural Selection.'" In *The Contemporary Review*, LXIII (February-March, 1893), 154-166, 439-456.

. . . The title of Mr. Darwin's great work furnishes us with an instance of the misleading effects produced by [metaphors]. . . . Here are two figures of speech which conspire to produce an impression more or less erroneous. The expression "natural selection" was chosen as serving to indicate some parallelism with artificial selection—the selection exercised by breeders. Now selection connotes volition, and thus gives to the thoughts of readers a wrong bias. Some increase of this bias is produced by the words in the second title, "favoured races;" for anything which is favoured implies the existence of some agent conferring a favour. I do not mean that Mr. Darwin himself failed to recognise the misleading connotations of his words, or that he did not avoid being misled by them. In chapter iv. of the "Origin of Species" he says that, considered literally, "natural selection is a false term," and that the personification of Nature is objectionable; but he thinks that readers, and those who adopt his views, will soon learn to guard themselves against the wrong implications. Here I venture to think that he was mistaken. . . .[159] . . .

. . . Artificial selection can pick out a particular trait, and, regardless of other traits of the individuals displaying it, can increase it by selective breeding in successive generations. For, to the breeder or fancier, it matters little whether such individuals are otherwise well constituted. . . . On the other hand, if we regard Nature as that which it is, an assemblage of various forces, inorganic and organic, some favourable to the maintenance of life and many at variance with its maintenance—forces which operate blindly—we see that there is no such selection of this or that trait, but that there is a selection only of individuals which are, by the aggregate of their traits, best fitted for living. . . . Now observe the fact which here chiefly concerns us, that survival of the fittest can increase any serviceable trait only if that trait conduces to prosperity of the individual, or of posterity, or of both, *in an important degree*. There can be no increase of any structure by natural selection unless, amid all the slightly varying structures constituting the organism, increase of this particular one is so advantageous as to cause greater multiplication of the family in which it arises than of other families. Variations which, though advantageous, fail to do this, must disappear again. Let us take a case.

Keenness of scent in a deer, by giving early notice of approaching enemies, subserves life so greatly that, other things equal, an individual having it in an unusual degree is more likely than others to [160] survive, and, among descendants, to leave some similarly endowed or more endowed, who again transmit the variation with, in some cases, increase. Clearly this highly useful power may be developed by natural selection. . . . But now suppose that one member of the herd—perhaps because of more efficient teeth, perhaps by greater muscularity of stomach, perhaps by secretion of more appropriate gastric juice—is enabled to eat and digest a not uncommon plant which the others refuse. This peculiarity may, if food is scarce, conduce to better self-maintenance, and better fostering of young, if the individual is a hind. But unless this plant is abundant, and the advantage consequently great, the advantages which other members of the herd gain from other slight variations may be equivalent. . . . That the variation giving the ability to eat a plant before unutilised, may become a trait of the herd, and eventually of the variety, it is needful that the individual in which it occurs shall have more descendants, or better descendants, or both, than have the various other individuals severally having their small superiorities. If these other individuals severally profit by their small superiorities, and transmit them to equally large numbers of offspring, no increase of the variation in question can take place: it must soon be cancelled. Whether in the "Origin of Species" Mr. Darwin has recognised this fact, I do not remember, but he has certainly done it by implication in his "Animals and Plants under Domestication.". . . That which survival of the fittest does in cases like the one I have instanced is to keep all faculties up to the mark, by destroying such as have faculties in some respect below the mark; and it can produce development of some one faculty only if that faculty is predominantly important. It seems to me that many naturalists have practically lost sight of this, and assume that natural selection will increase *any* advantageous trait. Certainly a view now widely accepted assumes as much. . . .[161]. . . .

Is it not then, as said above, that the use of the expression, "natural selection" has had seriously perverting effects? Must we not infer that there has been produced in the minds of naturalists, the tacit assumption that it can do what artificial selection does—can pick out and select any small advantageous trait; while it can, in fact, pick out no traits, but can only further the development of traits which, *in marked ways,* increase the general fitness for the conditions of existence? And is it not inferable that, failing to bear in mind the limiting condition, that to become established an advantageous variation must be such as will, other things remaining equal, add to the prosperity of the stirp,[1] many naturalists have been unawares led to espouse an untenable hypothesis? [166]. . . .

---

[1] Or "stirps," the total of any particular stock or race.

. . . It has been of late asserted, and by many believed, that inheritance of acquired characters cannot occur. Weismann,[2] they say, has shown that there is early established in the evolution of each organism, such a distinctness between those component units which carry on the individual life and those which are devoted to maintenance of the species, that changes in the one cannot affect the other. . . .[446]. . . .

. . . The alleged independence of the reproductive cells does not exist. . . . The reproductive cells are nothing more than portions of [the "soma," or aggregate of body cells] separated some little time before they are required to perform their functions.

Thus the theory of Weismann is doubly disproved. Inductively we are shown that there *does* take place that communication of characters from the somatic cells to the reproductive cells, which he says cannot take place; and deductively we are shown that this communication is a natural sequence of connections between the two which he ignores: his various conclusions are deduced from a postulate which is untrue.

From the title of this essay, and from much of its contents, nine readers out of ten will infer that it is directed against the views of Mr. Darwin. They will be astonished on being told that, contrariwise, it is directed against the views of those who, in a considerable measure, dissent from Mr. Darwin. For the inheritance of acquired characters, which it is now the fashion in the biological world to deny, was, by Mr. Darwin, fully recognised and often insisted on. Such of the foregoing arguments as touch Mr. Darwin's views, simply imply that the cause of evolution which at first he thought unimportant, but the importance of which he increasingly perceived as he grew older, is more important than he admitted even at the last. The neo-Darwinists, however, do not admit this cause at all.

Let it not be supposed that this explanation implies any disapproval of the dissentients, considered as such. Seeing how little regard for authority I have myself usually shown, it would be absurd in me to reflect in any degree upon those who have rejected certain of Mr. Darwin's teachings, for reasons which they have thought sufficient. But while their independence of thought is to be applauded rather than blamed, it is, I think, to be regretted that they have not guarded themselves against a long-standing bias. It is a common trait of human nature to seek some excuse when found in the wrong. Invaded self-esteem sets up a defence, and anything is made to serve. Thus it happened that when geologists and biologists, previously holding that all kinds of organisms arose by special creations, surrendered to the battery opened upon them by "The Origin of Species," they sought to minimise their irrationality by pointing to irrationality on the other

---

[2] August Weismann (1834-1914), German biologist. See pp. 110-115.

side. "Well, at any rate, Lamarck was wrong." "It is clear that we were right in rejecting his doctrine." And so, by duly emphasising the fact that he overlooked "Natural Selection" as the chief cause, and by showing how erroneous were some of his interpretations, they succeeded in mitigating the sense of their own error. It is true their creed was [454] that at successive periods in the Earth's history, old Floras and Faunas had been abolished and others introduced; . . . And it is true that Lamarck, while he rejected this absurd creed, assigned for the facts reasons some of which are absurd. But in consequence of the feeling described, his defensible belief was forgotten and only his indefensible ones remembered. This one-sided estimate has become traditional; so that there is now often shown a subdued contempt for those who suppose that there can be any truth in the conclusions of a man whose general conception was partly sense, at a time when the general conceptions of his contemporaries were wholly nonsense. Hence results unfair treatment—hence result the different dealings with the views of Lamarck and of Weismann.

"Where are the facts proving the inheritance of acquired characters"? ask those who deny it. Well, in the first place, there might be asked the counter-question—Where are the facts which disprove it? Surely if not only the general structure of organisms, but also many of the modifications arising in them, are inheritable, the natural implication is that all modifications are inheritable; and if any say that the inheritableness is limited to those arising in a certain way, the *onus* lies on them of proving that those otherwise arising are not inheritable. . . .

Finally, there comes the reply that there *are* facts proving the inheritance of acquired characters. All those assigned by Mr. Darwin, together with others such, remain outstanding when we find that [455] the interpretation by *panmixia* [3] is untenable. . . .

See, then, how the case stands. Natural selection, or survival of the fittest, is almost exclusively operative throughout the vegetal world and throughout the lower animal world; characterised by relative passivity. But with the ascent to higher types of animals, its effects are in increasing degree involved with those produced by inheritance of acquired characters; until, in animals of complex structures, inheritance of acquired characters becomes an important, if not the chief, cause of evolution. We have seen that natural selection cannot work any changes in organisms save such as conduce in considerable degrees, directly or indirectly, to the multiplication of the stirp; whence failure to account for various changes ascribed to it. And we have seen that it yields no explanation of the co-adaptation of co-operative parts, even when the co-operation is relatively simple, and still less when it

---

[3] Weismann's hypothesis of "reversed selection," involving the degeneration of organs.

is complex. On the other hand, we see that if, along with the transmission of generic and specific structures, there tend to be transmitted modifications arising in a certain way, there is a strong *a priori* probability that there tend to be transmitted modifications arising in all ways. We have a number of facts confirming this inference, and showing that acquired characters *are* inherited—as large a number as can be expected, considering the difficulty of observing them and the absence of search. . . .[456]

From "A Rejoinder to Professor Weismann." In *The Contemporary Review*, LXIV (December, 1893), 893-912.

The title of his [Weismann's] article [1] is "The All-sufficiency of Natural Selection." Very soon, however, as on p. 322, we come to the admission, which he has himself italicised, "that *it is really very difficult to imagine this process of natural selection in its details;* and to this day it is impossible to demonstrate it in any one point." Elsewhere, as on pp. 327 and 336 *à propos* of other cases, there are like admissions. But now if the sufficiency of an assigned cause cannot in any case be demonstrated, and if it is "really very difficult to imagine" in what way it has produced its alleged effects, what becomes of the "all-sufficiency" of the cause? How can its all-sufficiency be alleged when its action can neither be demonstrated nor easily imagined? Evidently to fit Professor Weismann's argument the title of the article should have been "The Doubtful Sufficiency of Natural Selection.". . .[893]. . . .

It is curious what entirely opposite conclusions men may draw from the same evidence. Professor Weismann thinks he has shown that the "last bulwark of the Lamarckian principle is untenable." Most readers will hold with me that he is, to use the mildest word, premature in so thinking. Contrariwise my impression is that he has not shown either this bulwark or any other bulwark to be untenable; but rather that while his assault has failed it has furnished opportunity for strengthening sundry of the bulwarks.[912]

---

[1] In the September and October (1893) numbers of *The Contemporary Review.* See pp. 110-113.

George J. Romanes (1848-1894)

From "Mr. Herbert Spencer on 'Natural Selection.'" In *The Contemporary Review,* LXIII (April, 1893), 499-517.

As the first evolutionist who seems to have questioned the belief in "Use-inheritance," and has closely followed all subsequent literature upon the subject, I should like to say a few words on the most recent contribution to this discussion by Mr. Herbert Spencer.

First of all it is desirable to furnish a brief sketch of the history of the issue "Natural Selection" *versus* "Lamarckian Factors," as this will be the shortest way of gaining a clear view of the sundry principles which that issue now involves.

In Darwin's judgment there were three distinct lines of evidence in favour of the Lamarckian Factors, namely, evidence furnished by (A) the apparently inherited effects of use and disuse; (B) by certain general considerations; and (C) by certain special experiments. . . .

A. Inherited Effects of Use and Disuse

There is no doubt that Darwin everywhere attaches great weight to this line of evidence. Nevertheless, in my opinion, there is equally little doubt that, taken by itself, it is of much less weight than Darwin supposed and Spencer still supposes. Indeed, I quite agree with Weismann that the whole of this line of evidence is practically worthless. . . .[499] . . .

. . . Darwin recognised that his whole line of evidence in favour of the Lamarckian Factors which we are here considering (viz., the line A) was seriously invalidated. His last edition of the "Origin of Species" had . . . been published, so he was unable to discuss the matter in that work, but in conversation he satisfied me that there still remained, in the lines B and C, independent evidence of the transmission of acquired characters sufficient to leave the general structure of his previous theory unaffected by what he nevertheless accepted as a necessarily additional factor, and one which was virtually destructive of the line A. . . .[501] . . .

B. General Considerations

It is satisfactory to pass from Mr. Spencer's treatment of the line of evidence A to his treatment of the line of evidence B. For more than any other writer, he has brought valid arguments to bear in this line—the line of general reasoning. . . .

(1) *Co-adaptation*

I have nothing further to supply touching [the] . . . argument [of co-adaptation of bodily organs]. For many years I have followed Mr. Spencer in representing it as an exceedingly cogent argument against Weismann, Wallace, and all ultra-Darwinians, who regard Natural Selection as "the exclusive means of modification." As long ago as 1888, Weismann promised [507] to answer what I had then said, but hitherto this promise has not been redeemed. Subsequently, Mr. Wallace gave a very lame answer in his "Darwinism.". . . The argument in question has been repeatedly brought before the notice of the ultra-Darwinians, with the result that it stands more firmly than ever. . . .[508]. . . .

. . . We all agree that Natural Selection is a true cause of adaptive modification in species, while we do not all agree that such is the case with the so-called Lamarckian Factors; hence it is for those who believe in those factors to give reasons for the faith that is in them. What, then, is the true logical standing of the issue as a whole? It would appear to be as follows:

All Neo-Darwinians will doubtless agree [on the following points]. . . . We may not needlessly multiply hypothetical causes in our explanations of given results; Natural Selection is a known cause of adaptive modification in species; the Lamarckian Factors are but hypothetical causes; besides, they are not necessary; therefore, away with them.

To this the Neo-Lamarckians may legitimately answer: True, we may not needlessly multiply hypothetical causes; but our position is that the causes in question are neither hypothetically adduced nor needlessly entertained. On the contrary, we believe that there is a large body of evidence in proof of their occurrence; and we further believe that, but for their occurrence, the process of organic evolution could never have been what it has been. Our adversaries seem to forget that the question in debate is the very question which they quietly beg, viz., as to whether Lamarckian doctrines are void of evidence and unnecessary, or sustained by facts and indispensable.

So far it is evident that the Neo-Lamarckians have the best of the argument. Indeed it cannot be said that so far their opponents are advancing any argument at all. When Darwin himself so emphatically held that the Lamarckian Factors are not only well substantiated by evidence, but are also necessary as supplements to Natural Selection,[516] the *onus* is clearly as much on the side of Neo-Darwinians to show that his opinion was wrong, as it is on the side of his followers to show that his opinion was right.

How, then, does the matter stand when we pass from these merely antecedent grounds of logic, to the real battlefield of facts? Here the questions are three in number. (1) Do we meet with facts in organic nature which cannot be explained by the theory of Natural Selection? (2) Are any of these facts capable of being explained by the theory of Use-inheritance? And (3), Is there any further evidence in favour of this theory? The answers to all these questions must be provisionally in the affirmative, at all events, until the Neo-Darwinians shall have more effectually disposed of the evidence already extant in the lines B and C. . . . Indeed, the facts which I have myself collected . . . and which I hope soon to publish, appear to me in themselves sufficient to prove that some principle of adaptive evolution, other than and supplementary to Natural Selection, must have been concerned in the production of organic types. Therefore, even if by means of their new theory of heredity [i.e., Weismann's germ-plasm theory and *panmixia*], or otherwise, the Neo-Darwinians should ever be able to disprove the possibility of use-inheritance, I should be driven to adopt the belief of Asa Gray, Nägeli,[1] Virchow,[2] and not a few other naturalists—the belief, I mean, that there is in nature some hitherto unknown principle of adoptive [adaptive?] modification, which is at present almost as unsuspected as was the principle of Natural Selection some half-century ago.[517]

⁓

From "A Note on Panmixia." In *The Contemporary Review*, LXIV (October, 1893), 611-612.

. . . Professor Weismann is not quite correct in saying that I adhere to the doctrine of the transmission of acquired characters. . . . My position with regard to this question is one of suspended judgment.

Ever since the time when I published the articles on the Cessation of Selection to which he refers, I have seen serious reasons for doubting the doctrine of use-inheritance. . . .[612]

⁓⁓⁓

August Weismann (1834-1914)

From "The All-Sufficiency of Natural Selection—A Reply to Herbert Spencer." In *The Contemporary Review*, LXIV (September-October, 1893), 309-338, 596-610.

Any one who has carefully studied the development of the problem of heredity in the course of the last ten years knows that my view of the intransmissibility of acquired characters has not yet received general assent and recognition among scientists. Many still

---

[1] Karl Wilhelm von Nägeli (1817-1891), Swiss-born botanist.
[2] Rudolf Virchow (1821-1902), German pathologist.

believe that such transmission can be proved; and not a year passes without some "convincing" instances being published. Most of these depend on imperfect comprehension of what is to be understood by an "acquired" character; . . .[309]. . . .

I will not . . . pause to refute . . . apparent proofs of the transmission of acquired characters; even were I to refute all that have hitherto been advanced, new ones would assuredly constantly be forthcoming; and so, arguing in this way, we should hardly come to a conclusion. Besides, I have ever contended that the acceptance of a principle of explanation is justified, if it can be shown that without it certain facts are inexplicable. I have therefore ever made it my task to show that the assumption of the transmission of acquired characters is not necessary for the explanation of known phenomena; and I have begun to render intelligible, apart from this belief, a large number of facts that have usually hitherto been only explained with its aid. . . .[311]. . . .

. . . Herbert Spencer is so thoroughly convinced of the strength of his argument [in favor of the transmission of acquired characters] that he goes the length of saying: "Either there has been inheritance of acquired characters, or there has been no evolution."

I am of a different opinion. Since I expressed the belief ten years ago, that functional variations (acquired characters) could not be transmitted, I have not ceased to test that view, and whenever I have been able to get a more thorough understanding of the facts, I have found it confirmed. But I freely grant that Mr. Spencer's objection is a tempting one; and I should not be surprised if many who read his essay, and are familiar with the enormous difficulties, which, according to his view, stand in the way of an explanation of the facts in question [312] through natural selection, should be carried away by the strength of his skilful representation, and hold the *easier* explanation of the facts—by the inheritance of acquired characters—to be the *correct* one.

I hope to show, however, that it *cannot* be the correct one, and that we must . . . set aside the apparently simple and almost matter-of-course explanation, and seek another. . . .[313]. . . .

. . . We shall never be able to establish by observation the progress of natural selection.[327]

What is it then that nevertheless makes us believe in this progress as actual, and leads us to ascribe such extraordinary importance to it? Nothing but the power of logic; we must assume natural selection to be the principle of explanation of the metamorphoses, because all other apparent principles of explanation fail us, and it is inconceivable that there could be yet another capable of explaining the adaptations of organisms, *without assuming the help of a principle of design*. In other words, *it is the only conceivable natural explanation of organisms regarded as adaptations to conditions*. . . .[328]. . . .

I myself was led to the discovery of the principle of Panmixia through serious doubt as to transmission of acquired characters. If there was no such transmission, then there must be another cause of the disappearance of useless parts to be discovered; and so I was led to Panmixia. When I was compelled to deny both the transmission of functional atrophy and the transmission of the effects of the principle of economy in the individual ontogeny, the new principle was at once demonstrated as active: there remained for me only the *one* explanation of organs becoming rudimentary, that of selection, either *negative* selection alone (Panmixia), or with the aid of *positive* selection, which prefers, and gives the victory to, the less injurious. . . .[335] . . .

. . . We must consider with what right we may look upon natural selection as the active factor [in producing harmoniously interacting parts in ant-workers].

The answer is very simple: *with the same right as we have for believing in its activity anywhere else in nature.* As already indicated, we accept it, not because we can with more or less ease imagine it, but simply *because we must, because it is the only possible explanation* that we can conceive. For there are only two possible *a priori* explanations of adaptations for the naturalist—namely, the transmission of functional adaptations and natural selection; but as the first of these can be excluded, only the second remains. . . .[336] . . .

. . . We are justified in . . . concluding that if . . . the struggle for existence acts as natural selection assumes it to act, that is, like the breeder who in artificial selection chooses what suits him, then *even the small variations which occur in all parts of the body may possess selection value;* . . . in other words, *natural selection effects all manner of adaptations.* . . .[337] . . .

. . . I hold it to be demonstrated that all hereditary adaptation rests on natural selection, and that natural selection is the one great principle that enables organisms to conform, to a certain high degree, to their varying conditions, by constructing new adaptations out of old ones. It is not merely an accessory principle, which only comes into operation when the assumed transmission of functional variation fails; but it is the chief principle in the variation of organisms, and compared to it, the primary variation which is due to the direct action of external influences on the germ-plasm, is of very secondary importance. . . . Therefore I hold the discovery of natural selection to be one of the most fundamental ever made in the field of biology, and one that is alone sufficient to immortalise the names of Charles Darwin and Alfred Wallace. When my opponents set me down as an ultra-Darwinist, who takes a one-sided and exaggerated view of the principle discovered by the great naturalist, perhaps that may make an impression on some of the timid souls who always act on the supposition that the *juste-milieu* [1] is proper; but it seems to me that it is never

---

[1] Literally, "just mean"—happy medium or golden mean.

possible to say *a priori* how far-reaching a principle of explanation is: it must be tried first; and to have made such a trial has been my offence or my merit. Only very gradually have I learned the full scope of the principle of selection; and certainly I have been led beyond Darwin's conclusions. Progress in science usually involves a struggle against deep-seated prejudices: such was the belief in the transmission of acquired characters; and it is only now that it has fortunately been overcome that the full significance of natural selection can be discerned. Now, for the first time, consummation of the principle is possible; and so my work has not been to exaggerate, but to complete.[338]

〰

From "The Selection Theory." Trans. Mrs. J. A. Thomson. In *Darwin and Modern Science: Essays in Commemoration of the Centenary of the Birth of Charles Darwin and of the Fiftieth Anniversary of the Publication of "The Origin of Species."* Ed. A. C. Seward. Cambridge, England: Cambridge University Press, 1909. Reprinted by permission of the publisher.

III. OBJECTIONS TO THE THEORY OF SELECTION

(a) *Saltatory* [1] *evolution*

The Darwinian doctrine of evolution depends essentially on *the cumulative augmentation* of minute variations in the direction of utility. But can such minute variations, which are undoubtedly continually appearing among the individuals of the same species, possess any selection-value; can they determine which individuals are to survive, and which are to succumb; can they be increased by natural selection till they attain to the highest development of a purposive variation?

To many this seems so improbable that they have urged a theory of evolution by leaps from species to species. . . .[22]. . . .

In recent years Bateson [2] in particular has championed the idea of saltatory, or so-called discontinuous evolution, and has collected a number of cases in which more or less marked variations have suddenly appeared. . . .[23]. . . .

---

[1] Jumping or leaping. See Glossary.
[2] William Bateson (1861-1926), English biologist. See pp. 124-126.

. . . H. de Vries [3] . . . believes that the roots of transformation must be sought for in *saltatory variations arising from internal causes,* and distinguishes such *mutations,* as he has called them, from ordinary individual variations, in that they breed true, that is, with strict inbreeding they are handed on pure to the next generation. I have elsewhere endeavoured to point out the weaknesses of this theory, and I am the less inclined to return to it here that it now appears that the far-reaching conclusions drawn by de Vries from his observations on the Evening Primrose, *Oenothera lamarckiana,* rest upon a very insecure foundation. . . .

Thus we come to the conclusion that Darwin was right in regarding transformations as taking place by minute steps, which, if useful,[24] are augmented in the course of innumerable generations, because their possessors more frequently survive in the struggle for existence. . . .[25] . . .

(c) *Co-adaptation*

Herbert Spencer, though himself an adherent of the theory of selection, declared in the beginning of the nineties that in his opinion the range of this principle was greatly over-estimated, if the great changes which have taken place in so many organisms in the course of ages are to be interpreted as due to this process of selection alone, since no transformation of any importance can be evolved by itself; it is always accompanied by a host of secondary changes. . . .[32] . . .

Spencer's main object was to substantiate the validity of the Lamarckian principle, the cooperation of which with selection had been doubted by many. And it does seem as though this principle, if it operates in nature at all, offers a ready and simple explanation of all such secondary variations. . . .

But beautiful as this explanation would be, I regard it as untenable, because it assumes the *transmissibility of functional modifications* (so-called "acquired" characters), and this is not only undemonstrable, but is scarcely theoretically conceivable, for the secondary variations which accompany or follow the first as correlative variations, occur also in cases in which the animals concerned are sterile and *therefore cannot transmit anything to their descendants.* . . .

Much has been written on both sides of this question since the published controversy on the subject in the nineties between Herbert Spencer and myself. I should like to return to the matter in detail, if the space at my disposal permitted, because it seems to me that the arguments I advanced at that time are equally cogent to-day, notwithstanding all the objections that have since been urged against them. . . .[33] . . .

But if it be asked why we are unwilling to admit the cooperation

---

[3] Hugo de Vries (1848-1935), Dutch botanist. See pp. 120-123.

of the Darwinian factor of selection and the Lamarckian factor, since this would afford us an easy and satisfactory explanation of the phenomena, I answer: *Because the Lamarckian principle is fallacious, and because by accepting it we close the way towards deeper insight.* It is not a spirit of combativeness or a desire for self-vindication that induces me to take the field once more against the Lamarckian principle, it is the conviction that the progress of our knowledge is being obstructed by the acceptance of this fallacious principle, since the facile explanation it apparently affords prevents our seeking after a truer explanation and a deeper analysis. . . .[34]. . . .

V. ARGUMENTS FOR THE REALITY OF THE PROCESSES OF SELECTION

(b) *Natural Selection*

. . . Whether the *Lamarckian principle* is a factor that has cooperated with selection in evolution, or whether it is altogether fallacious, the fact remains, that selection is the cause of a great part of the phyletic evolution of organisms on our earth. Those who agree with me in rejecting the *Lamarckian principle* will regard selection as the only *guiding* factor in evolution, which creates what is new out of the transmissible variations, by ordering and arranging these, selecting them in relation to their number and size, as the architect does his building-stones so that a particular style must result. . . .[65]

∽∽∽

Ernst Haeckel (1834-1919)

From "Charles Darwin as an Anthropologist." Trans. Joseph McCabe. In *Darwin and Modern Science* (for full title see p. 113). Reprinted by permission of the publisher.

Transformative heredity—or the transmission of acquired characters—is one of the most important principles in evolutionary science. Unless we admit it most of the facts of comparative anatomy and physiology are inexplicable. That was the conviction of Darwin no less than of Lamarck, of Spencer as well as Virchow,[1] of Huxley as well as Gegenbaur,[2] indeed of the great majority of speculative biologists. This fundamental principle was for the first time called in

---

1 See p. 110, footnote 2.
2 Karl Gegenbaur (1826-1903), German comparative anatomist.

question and assailed in 1885 by August Weismann of Freiburg, the eminent zoologist to whom the theory of evolution owes a great deal of valuable support, and who has attained distinction by his extension of the theory of selection. In explanation of the phenomena of heredity he introduced a new theory, the "theory of the continuity of the germ-plasm.". . .[139] . . .

This theory . . . has been expounded by Weismann during the last twenty-four years in a number of able volumes, and is regarded by many biologists . . . as the most striking advance in evolutionary science. On the other hand, the theory has been rejected by Herbert Spencer . . . and many others. For my part I have, with all respect for the distinguished Darwinian, contested the theory from the first, because its whole foundation seems to me erroneous, and its deductions do not seem to be in accord with the main facts of comparative morphology and physiology. Weismann's theory in its entirety is a finely conceived molecular hypothesis, but it is devoid of empirical basis. The notion of the absolute and permanent independence of the germ-plasm, as distinguished from the soma-plasm, is purely speculative; as is also the theory of germinal selection. . . .

It seems to me quite improper to describe this hypothetical structure as "Neodarwinism." Darwin was just as convinced as Lamarck of the transmission of acquired characters and its great importance in the scheme of evolution. I had the good fortune to visit Darwin at Down three times and discuss with him the main principles of his system, and on each occasion we were fully agreed as to the incalculable importance of what I call transformative inheritance. It is only proper to point out that Weismann's theory of the germ-plasm is in express contradiction to the fundamental principles of Darwin and Lamarck. Nor is it more acceptable in what one may call its "ultradarwinism"— the idea that the theory of selection explains everything in the evolution of the organic world. This belief in the "omnipotence of natural selection" was not shared by Darwin himself. Assuredly, I regard it as of the utmost value, as the process of natural selection through the struggle for life affords an explanation of the mechanical origin of the adapted organisation. It solves the great problem: how could the [140] finely adapted structure of the animal or plant body be formed unless it was built on a preconceived plan? It thus enables us to dispense with the teleology of the metaphysician and the dualist, and to set aside the old mythological and poetic legends of creation. The idea had occurred in vague form to the great Empedocles [3] 2000 years before the time of Darwin, but it was reserved for modern research to give it ample expression. Nevertheless, natural selection does not of itself give the solution of all our evolutionary problems. It has to be taken

---

[3] Greek philosopher, fifth century B.C.

in conjunction with the transformism of Lamarck, with which it is in complete harmony.

The monumental greatness of Charles Darwin, who surpasses every other student of science in the nineteenth century by the loftiness of his monistic conception of nature and the progressive influence of his ideas, is perhaps best seen in the fact that not one of his many successors has succeeded in modifying his theory of descent in any essential point or in discovering an entirely new standpoint in the interpretation of the organic world. . . . The "mutation-theory" of De Vries, that would explain the origin of species by sudden and saltatory variations rather than by gradual modification, is regarded by many botanists as a great step in advance, but it is generally rejected by zoologists. It affords no explanation of the facts of adaptation, and has no causal value. . . .[141]. . . .

If I have succeeded in furthering, in some degree, . . . the solution of the great problem of Man's place in nature, and particularly in helping to trace the definite stages in our ancestral series, I owe the success, not merely to the vast progress that biology has made in the last half century, but largely to the luminous example of the great investigators who have applied themselves to the problem, with so much assiduity and genius, for a century and a quarter—I mean Goethe [4] and Lamarck, Gegenbaur and Huxley, but, above all, Charles Darwin. It was the great genius of Darwin that first brought together the scattered material of biology and shaped it into that symmetrical temple of scientific knowledge, the theory of descent. It was Darwin who put the crown on the edifice by his theory of natural selection. Not until this broad inductive law was firmly established was it possible to vindicate the special conclusion, the descent of man from a series of other Vertebrates. . . .[149]. . . .

To appreciate fully the immortal merit of Darwin in connection with anthropology, we must remember that not only did his chief work, *The Origin of Species,* which opened up a new era in natural history in 1859, sustain the most virulent and widespread opposition for a lengthy period, but even thirty years later, when its principles were generally recognised and adopted, the application of them to man was energetically contested by many high scientific authorities. Even Alfred Russel Wallace . . . did not concede that it was applicable to the higher mental and moral qualities of man. Dr. Wallace still holds a spiritualist and dualist view of the nature of man, contending that he is composed of a material frame (descended from the apes) and an immortal immaterial soul (infused by a higher power). This dual conception, moreover, is still predominant in the wide circles of modern theology and metaphysics, and has the general and influential adherence of the more conservative classes of society.

---

[4] See p. 46, footnote 5.

In strict contradiction to this mystical dualism, which is generally connected with teleology and vitalism, Darwin always maintained the complete unity of human nature, and showed convincingly that the psychological side of man was developed, in the same way as the body, from the less advanced soul of the anthropoid ape, and, at a still more remote period, from the cerebral functions of the older vertebrates. . . .[150] . . . .

2. The Impact of Genetics on Darwinism

Intramural conflicts among Darwinians of whatever persuasion dissolved under the impact of Mendelism or, as it ultimately came to be called, the science of genetics. In 1900, the Dutch botanist Hugo de Vries, the German botanist Karl Correns, and the Austrian botanist Erich von Tschermak-Seysenegg independently rediscovered the principles of hereditary transmission which had been originally formulated and published in 1866 by the Austrian monk Gregor Mendel. Mendel's laws of segregation and dominance prepared the way for De Vries' mutation theory, though that theory was also anticipated by the concept of "discontinuous variation" developed before the end of the century by the British biologist William Bateson. Mendelism also led to the explanation of the mechanism of heredity in terms of chromosomes and genes by the American Thomas H. Morgan and others; to the application of mathematics to the problem of heredity by biometricians like Sir Ronald A. Fisher; and to the working-out of what Sir Julian S. Huxley calls a "modern synthesis" of the leading theories of organic evolution.

Hugo de Vries (1848-1935)

From *Species and Varieties—Their Origin by Mutation*. Ed. Daniel Trembly MacDougal. 2nd ed. Chicago: The Open Court Publishing Co. London: Kegan, Paul, Trench, Trübner & Co., 1906. Reprinted by permission of the publisher.

PREFACE BY THE AUTHOR:

The purpose of these lectures is to point out the means and methods by which the origin of species and varieties may become an object for experimental inquiry, in the interest of agricultural and horticultural practice as well as in that of general biologic science. Comparative studies have contributed all the evidence hitherto adduced for the support of the Darwinian theory of descent and given us some general ideas about the main lines of the pedigree of the vegetable kingdom, but the way in which one species originates from another has not been adequately explained. The current belief assumes that species are slowly changed into new types. In contradiction to this conception the theory of mutation assumes that new species and varieties are produced from existing forms by sudden leaps. The parent-type itself remains unchanged throughout this process, and may repeatedly give birth to new forms. These may arise simultaneously and in groups or separately at more or less widely distant periods.

The principal features of the theory of mutation have been dealt with at length in my book "Die Mutationstheorie" (Vol. I., 1901, Vol. II., 1903. Leipsic, Veit & Co.), in which I endeavored to present as completely as possible the detailed evidence obtained from trustworthy historical records, and from my own experimental researches, upon which the theory is based.

The University of California invited me to deliver a series of lectures on this subject, at Berkeley, during the [vii] summer of 1904, and these lectures are offered in this form to a public now thoroughly interested in the progress of modern ideas on evolution. . . . [viii] . . . .

LECTURE I—"DESCENT: THEORIES OF EVOLUTION, AND METHODS OF INVESTIGATION"

. . . Mendel's [1] claim of hereditary units for the explanation of certain laws of hybrids discovered by him, was not yet made [when Darwin formulated his theories]. The clear distinction between spon-

---

[1] Gregor Johann Mendel (1822-1884), Austrian monk and botanist, who established the theoretical basis for the science of genetics. The reader will note repeated references to Mendel and Mendelism throughout the entire last section of this book.

taneous and sudden changes, as compared with the ever-present fluctuating variations, is only of late coming into recognition by agricul-
turists. Innumerable minor points which go to elucidate the breeders'
experience, and with which we are now quite familiar, were unknown
in Darwin's time. No wonder that he made mistakes, and laid stress
on modes of descent, which have since been proved to be of minor
importance or even of doubtful validity. . . .[6]. . . .

   . . . One means of change lies in the sudden and spontaneous
production of new forms from the old stock. The other method is the
gradual accumulation of those always present and ever fluctuating
variations which are indicated by the common assertion that no two
individuals of a given race are exactly alike. The first changes are
what we now call "mutations," the second are designated as "individual variations," or as this term is often used in another sense, as
"fluctuations." Darwin recognized both lines of evolution; Wallace
disregarded the sudden changes and proposed fluctuations [7] as the
exclusive factor. Of late, however, this point of view has been abandoned by many investigators, especially in America.

   The actual occurrence of mutations is now recognized, and the
battle rages about the question, as to whether they are [to] be regarded as the principal means of evolution, or, whether slow and
gradual changes have not also played a large and important part.

   The defenders of the theory of evolution by slow accumulation
of slight fluctuations are divided into two camps. One group is called
the Neo-Lamarckians; they assume a direct modifying agency of the
environment, producing a corresponding and useful change in the
organization. The other group call themselves Darwinians or selec-
tionists, but to my mind with no right beyond the arbitrary restriction
of the Darwinian principles by Wallace. They assume fluctuating
variations in all directions and leave the choice between them to the
sieve of natural selection.

   Of course we are far from a decision between these two views, on
the sole ground of the facts as known at present. Mutations under
observation are as yet very rare; enough to indicate the possible and
most probable ways, but no more. On the other hand the accumulation of fluctuations does not transgress relatively narrow [8] limits as
far as the present methods of selection go. But the question remains
to be solved, whether our methods are truly the right ones, and
whether by the use of new principles, new results might not cause the
balance of opinion to favor the opposite side. . . .[9]. . . .

   . . . One of the greatest objections to the Darwinian theory of
descent arose from the length of time it would require, if all evolution was to be explained on the theory of slow and nearly invisible
changes. This difficulty is at once met and fully surmounted by the
hypothesis of periodical but sudden and quite noticeable steps. This
assumption requires only a limited number of mutative periods, which

might well occur within the time allowed by physicists and geologists for the existence of animal and vegetable life on the earth.[29]

. . . I shall try to prove that sudden mutation is the normal way in which nature produces new species and new varieties. These mutations are more readily accessible to observation and experiment than the slow and gradual changes surmised by Wallace and his followers, which are entirely beyond our present and future experience.

The theory of mutations is a starting-point for direct investigation, while the general belief in slow changes has held back science from such investigations during half a century. . . .[30]. . . .

᭜

From "Variation." In *Darwin and Modern Science* (for full title see p. 113). Reprinted by permission of the publisher.

Some authors have tried to show that the theory of mutation is opposed to Darwin's views. But this is erroneous. On the contrary,[73] it is in fullest harmony with the great principle laid down by Darwin. In order to be acted upon by that complex of environmental forces, which Darwin has called natural selection, the changes must obviously first be there. The manner in which they are produced is of secondary importance and has hardly any bearing on the theory of descent with modification.

A critical survey of all the facts of variability of plants in nature as well as under cultivation has led me to the conviction, that Darwin was right in stating that those rare beneficial variations, which from time to time happen to arise—the now so-called mutations—are the real source of progress in the whole realm of the organic world. . . .[74]. . . .

Mutating variability occurs along three main lines. Either a character may disappear, or, as we now say, become latent; or a latent character may reappear, reproducing thereby a character which was once prominent in more or less remote ancestors. The third and most interesting case is that of the production of quite new characters which never existed in the ancestors. Upon this progressive mutability the main development of the animal and vegetable kingdom evidently depends. In contrast to this, the two other cases are called retrogressive and degressive mutability. In nature retrogressive mutability plays a large part; in agriculture [75] and in horticulture it gives rise to numerous varieties, which have in the past been preserved, either on account of their usefulness or beauty, or simply as fancy-types. In fact the possession of numbers of varieties may be considered as the main character of domesticated animals and cultivated plants.

In the case of retrogressive and degressive mutability the internal cause is at once apparent, for it is this which causes the disappearance or reappearance of some character. With progressive mutations the case is not so simple, since the new character must first be produced and then displayed. These two processes are theoretically different, but they may occur together or after long intervals. The production of the new character I call premutation, and the displaying, mutation. Both of course must have their external as well as their internal causes, as I have repeatedly pointed out in my work on the Mutation Theory. . . .[76]. . . .

The origin of new species, which is in part the effect of mutability, is, however, due mainly to natural selection. Mutability provides the new characters and new elementary species. Natural selection, on the other hand, decides what is to live and what to die. Mutability seems to be free, and not restricted to previously determined lines. Selection, however, may take place along the same main lines in the course of long geological epochs, thus directing the development of large branches of the animal and vegetable kingdom. In natural selection it is evident that nutrition and environment are the main factors. But it is probable that, while nutrition may be one of the main causes of mutability, environment may play the chief part in the decisions ascribed to natural selection. Relations to neighbouring plants and to injurious or useful animals, have been considered the most important determining factors ever since the time when Darwin pointed out their prevailing influence. . . .[77]. . . .

Darwin has repeatedly insisted that man does not cause variability. He simply selects the variations given to him by the hand of nature. He may repeat this process in order to accumulate different new characters in the same family, thus producing varieties of a higher order. This process of accumulation would, if continued for a longer time, lead to the augmentation of the slight differences characteristic of varieties into the greater differences characteristic of species and genera. It is in this way that horticultural and agricultural experience contribute to the problem of the conversion of varieties into species, and to the explanation of the admirable adaptations of each organism to its complex conditions of life. In the long run new forms, distinguished from their allies by quite a number of new characters, would, by the extermination of the older intermediates, become distinct species.

Thus we see that the theory of the origin of species by means of [83] natural selection is quite independent of the question, how the variations to be selected arise. They may arise slowly, from simple fluctuations, or suddenly, by mutations; in both cases natural selection will take hold of them, will multiply them if they are beneficial, and in the course of time accumulate them, so as to produce that great diversity of organic life, which we so highly admire. . . .[84]

William Bateson (1861-1926)

From "Heredity and Variation in Modern Lights." In *Darwin and Modern Science* (for full title see p. 113). Reprinted by permission of the publisher.

Darwin's work has the property of greatness in that it may be admired from more aspects than one. For some the perception of the principle of Natural Selection stands out as his most wonderful achievement to which all the rest is subordinate. Others, among whom I would range myself, look up to him rather as the first who plainly distinguished, collected, and comprehensively studied that new class of evidence from which hereafter a true understanding of the process of Evolution may be developed. We each prefer our own standpoint of admiration; but I think that it will be in their wider aspect that his labours will most command the veneration of posterity. . . .[85] . . .

Why . . . was it, that Darwin succeeded where the rest [of his fellow-scientists] had failed? The cause of that success was two-fold. First, and obviously, in the principle of Natural Selection he had a suggestion which would work. It might not go the whole way, but it was true as far as it went. Evolution could thus in great measure be fairly represented as a consequence of demonstrable processes. Darwin seldom endangers the mechanism he devised by putting on it strains much greater than it can bear. He at least was under no illusion as to the omnipotence of Selection; and he introduces none of the forced pleading which in recent years has threatened to discredit that principle. . . .[87] . . .

. . . To learn the laws of Heredity and Variation there is no other way than that which Darwin himself followed, the direct examination of the phenomena. A beginning could be made by collecting fortuitous observations of this class, which have often thrown a suggestive light, but such evidence can be at best but superficial and some more penetrating instrument of research is required. This can only be provided by actual experiments in breeding.

The truth of these general considerations was becoming gradually clear to many of us when in 1900 Mendel's work was rediscovered. Segregation, a phenomenon of the utmost novelty, was thus revealed. From that moment not only in the problem of the origin of species, but in all the great problems of biology a new era began. So unexpected was the discovery that many naturalists were convinced it was untrue, and at once proclaimed Mendel's conclusions as either altogether mistaken, or if true, of very limited application. Many fantastic notions about the workings of Heredity had been asserted as general principles before: this was probably only another fancy of the same class.

Nevertheless those who had a preliminary acquaintance with the facts of Variation were not wholly unprepared for some such revelation. The essential deduction from the discovery of segregation was that the characters of living things are dependent on the presence of definite elements or factors, which are treated as units in the processes of Heredity. These factors can thus be recombined in various ways. They act sometimes separately, and sometimes they interact in conjunction with each other, producing their various effects. All this indicates a definiteness and specific order in heredity, and therefore in variation. This order cannot by the nature of the case be dependent on Natural Selection for its existence, but must be a consequence of the fundamental chemical and physical nature of living things. The study of Variation had from the first shown that an orderliness of this kind was present. The bodies and the properties of living things are cosmic, not chaotic. No matter how low in the scale we go, never do we find the slightest hint of a diminution in that all-pervading orderliness, nor can we conceive an organism existing for a moment in any other state. Moreover not only does this order prevail in normal forms, but again and again it is to be seen in newly-sprung varieties, which by general consent cannot have been subjected to a prolonged Selection. The discovery of Mendelian elements admirably coincided with and at once gave a rationale of these facts. Genetic Variation is then primarily the consequence of additions to, or omissions from, the stock of elements which the [92] species contains. The further investigation of the species-problem must thus proceed by the analytical method which breeding experiments provide. . . .[93] . . .

In the light of present knowledge it is evident that before we can attack the Species-problem with any hope of success there are vast arrears to be made up. He would be a bold man who would now assert that there was no sense in which the term Species might not have a strict and concrete meaning in contradistinction to the term Variety. We have been taught to regard the difference between species and variety as one of degree. I think it unlikely that this [94] conclusion will bear the test of further research. To Darwin the question, What is a variation? presented no difficulties. Any difference between parent and offspring was a variation. Now we have to be more precise. First we must, as de Vries has shown, distinguish real, genetic, variation from *fluctuational* variations, due to environmental and other accidents, which cannot be transmitted. Having excluded these sources of error the variations observed must be expressed in terms of the factors to which they are due before their significance can be understood. . . .[95] . . .

. . . We must relegate Selection to its proper place. Selection permits the viable to continue and decides that the nonviable shall perish; just as the temperature of our atmosphere decides that no liquid carbon shall be found on the face of the earth: but we do not suppose that the form of the diamond has been gradually achieved by a process of Selection. So again, as the course of descent branches in the successive generations, Selection determines along which branch Evolution shall proceed, but it does not decide what novelties that branch shall bring forth. . . .[96]. . . .

The question is sometimes asked, Do the new lights on Variation and Heredity make the process of Evolution easier to understand? On the whole the answer may be given that they do. There is some appearance of loss of simplicity, but the gain is real. As was said above, the time is not ripe for the discussion of the origin of species. With faith in Evolution unshaken—if indeed the word faith can be used in application to that which is certain—we look on the manner and causation of adapted differentiation as still wholly mysterious. As Samuel Butler so truly said: "To me it seems that the 'Origin of Variation,' whatever it is, is the only true 'Origin of Species' ", and of that Origin not one of us knows anything. But given Variation— and it is given: assuming further that the variations are not guided into paths of adaptation—and both to the Darwinian and to the modern school this hypothesis appears to be sound if unproven—an evolution of species proceeding by definite steps is more, rather than less, easy to imagine than an evolution proceeding by the accumulation of indefinite and insensible steps. Those who have lost themselves in contemplating the miracles of Adaptation (whether real or spurious) have not unnaturally fixed their hopes rather on the indefinite than on the definite changes. The reasons are obvious. By suggesting that the steps through which an adaptive mechanism arose were indefinite and insensible, all further trouble is spared. While it could be said that species arise by an insensible and imperceptible process of variation, there was clearly no use in tiring ourselves by trying to perceive that process. This labour-saving counsel found great favour. All that had to be done to develop evolution-theory was to discover the good in everything, a task which, in the complete absence of any control or test whereby to check the truth of the [99] discovery, is not very onerous. . . .[100]. . . .

No one can survey the work of recent years without perceiving that evolutionary orthodoxy developed too fast, and that a great deal has got to come down; but this satisfaction at least remains, that in the experimental methods which Mendel inaugurated, we have means of reaching certainty in regard to the physiology of Heredity and Variation upon which a more lasting structure may be built.[101]

Thomas H. Morgan (1866-1945)

From *A Critique of the Theory of Evolution.*
Princeton: Princeton University Press, 1916.
Reprinted by permission of the publisher.

CHAPTER I–"A REVALUATION OF THE EVIDENCE ON WHICH
THE THEORY OF EVOLUTION WAS BASED"

Darwin appealed to *chance variations* as supplying evolution with
the material on which natural selection works. If we accept, for the
moment, this statement as the cardinal doctrine of natural selection
it may appear that evolution is due, (1) *not* to an *orderly* response
of the organism to its environment, (2) *not* in the main to the activities
of the animal through the use or disuse of its parts, (3) *not* to any
innate principle of living material itself, and (4) above all *not* to
purpose either from within or from without. Darwin made quite clear
what he meant by chance. By chance he did not mean that the variations were not causal. On the contrary he taught that in Science we
mean by chance only that the particular combination of causes that
bring about a variation are not known. They are accidents, it is true,
but they are causal accidents.

In his famous book on "Animals and Plants under Domestication," Darwin dwells at great length on the nature of the conditions
that [37] bring about variations. If his views seem to us today at times
vague, at times problematical, and often without a secure basis,
nevertheless we find in every instance, that Darwin was searching for
the *physical causes of variation.* He brought, in consequence, conviction to many minds that there are abundant indications, even if
certain proof is lacking, that the causes of variation are to be found
in natural processes.

Today the belief that evolution takes place by means of natural
processes is generally accepted. It does not seem probable that we
shall ever again have to renew the old contest between evolution and
special creation.

But this is not enough. We can never remain satisfied with a
negative conclusion of this kind. We must find out what natural
causes bring about variations in animals and plants; and we must
also find out what kinds of variation are inherited, and how they are
inherited. If the circumstantial evidence for organic evolution, furnished by comparative anatomy, embryology and paleontology is
cogent, we should be able to observe evolution going on at [38] the
present time, i.e. we should be able to observe the occurrence of
variations and their transmission. This has actually been done by the
geneticist in the study of mutations and Mendelian heredity. . . .[39]

CHAPTER II—"THE BEARING OF MENDEL'S DISCOVERY ON THE ORIGIN OF HEREDITARY CHARACTERS"

Mutation and Evolution

What bearing has the appearance of . . . new types of Drosophila [1] on the theory of evolution may be asked. The objection has been raised in fact that in the breeding work with Drosophila we are dealing with artificial and unnatural conditions. It has been more than implied that results obtained from the breeding pen, the seed pan, the flower pot and the milk bottle do not apply to evolution in the "open," nature "at large" or to "wild" types. To be consistent, this same objection should be extended to the use of the spectroscope in the study of the evolution of the stars, to the use of the test tube and the balance by the chemist, of the galvanometer by the physicist. All these [84] are unnatural instruments used to torture Nature's secrets from her. I venture to think that the real antithesis is not between unnatural and natural treatment of Nature, but rather between controlled or verifiable data on the one hand, and unrestrained generalization on the other. . . .[85]. . . .

. . . Evolution of wild [86] species appears to have taken place by modifying and improving bit by bit the structures and habits that the animal or plant already possessed. We have seen that there are thirty mutant factors at least that have an influence on eye color, and it is probable that there are at least as many normal factors that are involved in the production of the red eye of the wild fly.

Evolution from this point of view has consisted largely in introducing new factors that influence characters already present in the animal or plant.

Such a view gives us a somewhat different picture of the process of evolution from the old idea of a ferocious struggle between the individuals of a species with the survival of the fittest and the annihilation of the less fit. Evolution assumes a more peaceful aspect. New and advantageous characters survive by incorporating themselves into the race, improving it and opening to it new opportunities. In other words, the emphasis may be placed less on the competition between the individuals of a species (because the destruction of the less fit does [87] not in itself lead to anything that is new) than on the appearance of new characters that become incorporated in the species, for on these depends the evolution of the race.[88]

CHAPTER IV—"SELECTION AND EVOLUTION"

How Does Natural Selection Influence the Course of Evolution?

The question still remains: Does selection play any role in evolution, and, if so, in what sense? Does the elimination of the unfit

---

[1] *Drosophila melanogaster*, the common fruit fly, used widely by Morgan and other geneticists for their breeding experiments.

influence the course of evolution, except in the negative sense of leaving more room for the fit? There is something further to be said in this connection, although opinions may differ as to whether the following interpretation of the term "natural selection" is the only possible one.

If through a mutation a character appears [187] that is neither advantageous nor disadvantageous, but indifferent, the chance that it may become established in the race is extremely small, although by good luck, such a thing may occur rarely. It makes no difference whether the character in question is a dominant or a [188] recessive one, the chance of its becoming established is exactly the same. If through a mutation a character appears that has an *injurious* effect, however slight this may be, it has practically no chance of becoming established.

If through a mutation a character appears that has a *beneficial* influence on the individual, the chance that the individual will survive is increased, not only for itself, but for all of its [189] descendants that come to inherit this character. It is this increase in the number of individuals possessing a particular character, that might have an influence on the course of evolution. This gives a better chance for improvement by several successive steps; but not because the species is more likely to mutate again in the same direction. An imaginary example will illustrate how this happens: When elephants had trunks less than a foot long, the chance of getting trunks more than one foot long was in proportion to the length of trunks already present and to the number of individuals; but increment in trunk length is no more likely to occur from an animal having a trunk more than one foot long than from an animal with a shorter trunk.

The case is analogous to tossing pennies. At any stage in the game the chance of accumulating a hundred heads is in proportion to the number of heads already obtained, and to the number of throws still to be made. But the number of heads obtained has no influence on the number of heads that will appear in the next throw.[190]. . . .

Owing then to this property of the germ plasm to duplicate itself in a large number of samples not only is an opportunity furnished to an advantageous variation to become extensively multiplied, but the presence of a large number of individuals of a given sort prejudices the probable future result.

The question may be raised as to whether it is desirable to call selection a *creative* process. There are so many supernatural and mystical implications that hang around the term creative that one can not be too careful in stating in what sense the term is to be used. If by creative is meant that something is made out of nothing, then of course there is no need for the scientist to try to answer such a question. But if by a creative process is meant that something is made out of something else, then there are two alternatives to be reckoned with.

First, if it were true that selection of an individual of a certain kind determines that new variations in the same direction occur as a consequence of the selection, then selection would certainly be creative. How this could occur might be quite unintelligible, but of course it [192] might be claimed that the point is not whether we can explain how creation takes place, but whether we can get verifiable evidence that such a kind of thing happens. This possibility is disposed of by the fact that there is no evidence that selection determines the direction in which variation occurs.

Second, if you mean by a creative process that by picking out a certain kind of individual and multiplying its numbers a better chance is furnished that a certain end result will be obtained, such a process may be said to be creative. This is, I think, the proper use of the term creative in a mechanistic sense.

Conclusions

In reviewing the evidence relating to selection I have tried to handle the problem as objectively as I could.

The evidence shows clearly that the characters of wild animals and plants, as well as those of domesticated races, are inherited both in the wild and in the domesticated forms according to Mendel's Law.

The causes of the mutations that give rise [193] to new characters we do not know, although we have no reason for supposing that they are due to other than natural causes.

Evolution has taken place by the incorporation into the race of those mutations that are beneficial to the life and reproduction of the organism. Natural selection as here defined means both the increase in the number of individuals that results after a beneficial mutation has occurred (owing to the ability of living matter to propagate) and also that this preponderance of certain kinds of individuals in a population makes some further results more probable than others. More than this, natural selection can not mean, if factors are fixed and are not changed by selection.[194]

From *Evolution and Genetics*. Princeton: Princeton University Press, 1925. (This volume is an amplification and revision of *A Critique of the Theory of Evolution*.) Reprinted by permission of the publisher.

CHAPTER VI—"THE CHROMOSOMES AND MENDEL'S TWO LAWS"

The discoveries that Mendel made with peas have been found to apply everywhere throughout the plant and animal kingdoms—to

flowering plants, to mosses, to insects, snails, crustacea, fishes, amphi-
bians, birds, and mammals (including man).

There must be something that these widely separated groups of
plants and animals have in common—some simple mechanism perhaps
—to give such definite and orderly series or results. There is, in fact,
a mechanism, possessed alike by animals and plants, that fulfils the
requirements of Mendel's principles. . . .[73]. . . .

The Cellular Basis of Heredity and Development

The egg is a cell, and the spermatazoon is a cell. Fertilization is
the union of two cells. Simple as the process of fertilization appears
to us today, its discovery swept aside a vast amount of mystical speculation concerning the role of the male and of the female in the act of
procreation.

Within the cell a new microcosm was revealed. Every cell was
found to contain a spherical body called the nucleus. Within the
nucleus is a network of fibres; a sap fills the interstices of the [74] network. The network resolves itself into a definite number of threads
or rods at each division of the cell. These rods we call chromosomes.
Each species of animals and plants possesses a characteristic number
of chromosomes which have a definite size, and sometimes a specific
shape, and even characteristic granules at different levels. Beyond this
point our strongest microscopes fail to penetrate.[75] Observation has
reached, for the time being, its limit.

Certain evidence relating to inheritance through the sperm led
to the conclusion that the chromosomes are the bearers of the hereditary units.[1] If so, there should be many such units carried by *each*
chromosome; [76] for, the number of chromosomes is limited while the
number of independently inherited characters is large. In Drosophila
melanogaster it has been demonstrated not only that there are exactly
as many groups of characters that are inherited together as there are
pairs of chromosomes, but even that it is possible to locate the hereditary elements in particular chromosomes and to state the relative
position there of the factors for the characters. If [77] the validity of
this evidence is accepted, the study of the cell leads to the ultimate
units about which the whole process of the transmission of the hereditary factors turns. . . .[78]. . . .

The Mechanism of Mendel's Two Laws

The behavior of the chromosomes at the time of maturation of
the egg- and sperm-cells furnishes a mechanism for Mendelian heredity
if the chromosomes are the bearers of the hereditary elements, and
if they maintain their integrity both during the resting [82] stages of
the nucleus and during their period of active division. There is a

---

[1] The genes.

great deal of evidence from direct observation in favor of this view and there is more evidence from the modern work in heredity that points in the same direction. . . .[83]. . . .

⁓⁓⁓

Ronald A. Fisher (1890-   )

From *The Genetical Theory of Natural Selection*. 2nd ed. New York: Dover Publications, Inc., 1958. (Published originally in 1930.) Reprinted by permission of the publisher.

PREFACE:

Natural Selection is not Evolution. Yet, ever since the two words have been in common use, the theory of Natural Selection has been employed as a convenient abbreviation for the theory of Evolution by means of Natural Selection, put forward by Darwin and Wallace. This has had the unfortunate consequence that the theory of Natural Selection itself has scarcely ever, if ever, received separate consideration. . . . The overwhelming importance of evolution to the biological sciences partly explains why the theory of Natural Selection should have been so fully identified with its role as an evolutionary agency, as to have suffered neglect as an independent principle worthy of scientific study.

The other biological theories which have been put forward, either as auxiliaries, or as the sole means of organic evolution, are not quite in the same position. For advocates of Natural Selection have not failed to point out, what was evidently the chief attraction of the theory to Darwin and Wallace, that it proposes to give an account of the means of modification in the organic world by reference only to 'known,' or independently demonstrable, causes. The alternative theories of modification rely, avowedly, on hypothetical properties of living matter which are inferred from the facts of evolution themselves. Yet, although this distinction has often been made clear, its logical cogency could never be fully developed in the absence of a separate investigation of the independently demonstrable modes of causation which are claimed as its basis. The present book, with all the limitations of a first attempt, is at least an attempt to consider the theory of Natural Selection on its own merits.

When the theory was first put forward, by far the vaguest element in its composition was the principle of inheritance. No man of learning or experience could deny this principle, yet, at the time, no approach could be given to an exact account of its working. That an [7li] independent study of Natural Selection is now possible is principally due to the great advance which our generation has seen in the science of genetics. . . .[viii]. . . .

In the future, the revolutionary effect of Mendelism will be seen to flow from the particulate character of the hereditary elements.[1] On this fact a rational theory of Natural Selection can be based, and it is, therefore, of enormous importance. The merit for this discovery must mainly rest with Mendel, whilst among our countrymen, Bateson played the leading part in its early advocacy. Unfortunately he was unprepared to recognize the mathematical or statistical aspects of biology, and from this and other causes he was not only incapable of framing an evolutionary theory himself, but entirely failed to see how Mendelism supplied the missing parts of the structure first erected by Darwin. His interpretation of Mendelian facts was from the first too exclusively coloured by his earlier belief in the discontinuous origin of specific forms. Though his influence upon [ix] evolutionary theory was thus chiefly retrogressive, the mighty body of Mendelian researches throughout the world has evidently outgrown the fallacies with which it was at first fostered. As a pioneer of genetics he has done more than enough to expiate the rash polemics of his early writings. . . .[x]

CHAPTER I—"THE NATURE OF INHERITANCE"

Summary

The tacit assumption of the blending theory of inheritance [2] led Darwin, by a perfectly cogent argument, into a series of speculations, respecting the causes of variations, and the possible evolutionary effects of these causes. In particular the blending theory, by the enormous mutation rates which it requires, led Darwin to some extent and others still more to attach evolutionary importance to hypothetical agencies which control the production of mutations. A mechanism [20] (Mendelism) of particulate inheritance has since been discovered, requiring mutations to an extent less by many thousandfold. . . . The nature of the mutations observed is not compatible with the view that evolution is directed by their means, while their observed frequency of occurrence shows that an agency controlling mutations would be totally ineffectual in governing the direction of evolutionary change.

The whole group of theories which ascribe to hypothetical physiological mechanisms, controlling the occurrence of mutations, a power of directing the course of evolution, must be set aside, once the

---

[1] The particulate theory of inheritance—implicit in Mendel's law of segregation—maintains that parental hereditary units retain their integrity or individuality when they combine to form offspring.

[2] The blending theory maintains that the heredity units "blend" or *lose* their individuality when they combine.

blending theory of inheritance is abandoned. The sole surviving theory is that of Natural Selection, and it would appear impossible to avoid the conclusion that if any evolutionary phenomenon appears to be inexplicable on this theory, it must be accepted at present merely as one of the facts which in the current state of knowledge does seem inexplicable. The investigator who faces this fact, as an unavoidable inference from what is now known of the nature of inheritance, will direct his inquiries confidently towards a study of the selective agencies at work throughout the life history of the group in their native habitats, rather than to speculations on the possible causes which influence their mutations. The experimental study of agencies capable of influencing mutation rates is of the highest interest for the light which it may throw on the nature of these changes. We should altogether misinterpret the value of such researches were we to regard them as revealing the causes of evolutionary modification.

Since the discovery of the means of releasing atomic energy, and the demonstration in 1945 of its immense potency in the destruction of life and property, considerable popular alarm has been promoted as to the possibility of injury to the human race due to mutations caused by various physical radiations arising from its utilization. Wholesale destruction is certainly terrible, but this is no reason for ascribing to the same cause in addition terrible consequences of an entirely hypothetical kind. In respect of human evolution, among the grave dangers to which the human species is exposed, mutations would seem to be among those least to be feared; moreover it is now known that mutagenic action is characteristic not only of high energy radiations, but of a wide variety of purely chemical agents.[21]

〜〜〜

Julian S. Huxley (1887-   )

From *Evolution: The Modern Synthesis*. New York and London: Harper & Brothers, 1942. Copyright 1942 by Julian S. Huxley. Reprinted by permission of the publisher.

CHAPTER I—"THE THEORY OF NATURAL SELECTION"

The Eclipse of Darwinism

Biology in the last twenty years, after a period in which new disciplines were taken up in turn and worked out in comparative isolation, has become a more unified science. It has embarked upon a period of synthesis, until to-day it no longer presents the spectacle of a number of semi-independent and largely contradictory sub-sciences, but is coming to rival the unity of older sciences like physics, in which advance in any one branch leads almost at once to advance in all other fields, and theory and experiment march hand-in-hand. As one chief result, there has been a rebirth of Darwinism. . . . It is noteworthy that T. H. Morgan, after having been one of the most extreme critics of selectionist doctrine, has recently, as a result of modern work in genetics (to which he has himself so largely contributed), again become an upholder of the Darwinian point of view (T. H. Morgan, 1925, and later writings); while [26] his younger colleagues, notably Muller [1] and Sturtevant,[2] are strongly selectionist in their evolutionary views.

The Darwinism thus reborn is a modified Darwinism, since it must operate with facts unknown to Darwin; but it is still Darwinism in the sense that it aims at giving a naturalistic interpretation of evolution, and that its upholders, while constantly striving for more facts and more experimental results, do not, like some cautious spirits, reject the method of deduction. . . .[27] . . . .

From "Darwin and the Idea of Evolution." In *A Book That Shook the World: Anniversary Essays on Charles Darwin's "Origin of Species."* Pittsburgh: University of Pittsburgh Press, 1958. Reprinted by permission of the publisher.

. . . [Darwin's] primary achievement lay in providing evidence for evolution, in demonstrating that the observable phenomena of biology made it impossible to believe in the stability of species in time, in a single original creation or in serial creation in relation with a succession of cataclysms; on the contrary, they indicated a slow transformation of types taking place over very long periods. He was the first to establish the fact of evolution on a firm basis. Here all later work has provided overwhelming confirmation. . . .

His other major achievement was the discovery of the principle of natural selection, which made the brute fact of evolution scientifically comprehensible. This has had a much more chequered history. There was a period when the principle was under heavy and indeed bitter attack, from the Lamarckians and the vitalists on the one hand,

---

[1] Hermann J. Muller (1890-   ), American zoologist and geneticist.
[2] Alfred H. Sturtevant (1891-   ), American zoologist and geneticist.

...he strict orthogeneticists [1] and the mutationists on the other. Natural selection was attacked by some as being too teleological; and by others because it depended solely on "chance," and therefore was not teleological enough to produce the apparently purposeful characters that everywhere confront the biologist. At one period it was maintained that though natural selection would have a negative effect, in pruning the species of deleterious variations, it could not have a positive effect and bring about directional transformation. And, it was urged, natural selection had never been experimentally proved to be operative.[2]

All these objections have now been met. We can not only point to cases where natural selection is operative in producing transformation or in maintaining adaptations, but can often measure its strength quantitatively. We know that it can produce positive as well as negative effects, and is the only agency which can bring about change (evolutionary transformation) in certain circumstances, no change in others. We have elaborate mathematical theories demonstrating how selection will operate in different circumstances. And we have proved that Lamarckian inheritance or inherent vital urges to change do not exist. . . .

The discoveries of genetics have got rid of Darwin's greatest difficulty. He (in common with many others, including the biometricians half a century later) thought that complete blending of the two parental types would occur in heredity, so that any new variation would tend to be diluted by crossing in each generation. . . . We know that inheritable variations are due to mutations, in other words to self-perpetuating changes of definite extent in the self-reproducing material units of the genetic constitution, the genes; and that blending of hereditary material never occurs. . . .[3] . . .

. . . Darwin himself regarded sexual selection as an important supplement to natural selection, though he erroneously imagined that it would be less rigorous and therefore less effective. New facts have led to considerable modifications in the theory. . . .[4] . . .

However, an important core of validity remains. Selection does operate to produce striking secondary sexual characters, but it is better called *intrasexual* than simply sexual. There is competition for reproductive success between the males of the same species. . . . Intrasexual intraspecific selection is supplementary to ordinary natural selection, and produces results of a new and different type.

. . . [In] *The Descent of Man* . . . [Darwin assembled] a large body of evidence to demonstrate that our species must have originated from an anthropoid ancestor. This conclusion, too, has been amply confirmed. . . .

---

[1] Orthogenesis refers to the evolution of living forms in response to some purposeful, internal cause, rather than to natural selection or other external causes.

Nor did Darwin shrink from applying evolutionary ideas to the development of "the mental qualities of animals," as he writes in the *Origin*. He never shirked the implications of evolution as regards mind, and never pretended that "mental qualities" did not exist in animals, nor tried to disguise their reality by a purely behaviourist terminology. . . .[5]. . . .

These general conclusions, too, have been beautifully established by the vast body of later research in this field. . . .

Alfred Russel Wallace himself called Darwin the Newton of biology. The appellation is deserved. Newton introduced order and unity into the physical world, Darwin into the biological world. And, just as Newtonian regularities spilled over into biology, so the evolutionary orderliness discovered by Darwin spilled over into the inorganic realm on the one hand, the human realm on the [6] other. It is not only for the profundity but for the universality of his ideas that we acknowledge Darwin's pre-eminence in the history of human thought.

Darwin's essential achievement was to establish the idea of evolution as a natural process. . . .

. . . If evolution is accepted as a fact, much of the *theological* framework of the world's major religions is destroyed, or is conveniently (but to my mind disingenuously) represented as significant myth. . . .

After Darwin . . . the idea of creation (including the Cuvierian [2] version of it which postulated a number of successive creations, separated by a series of cataclysms) had to be given up in favour of the gradual transformation, diversification, and improvement of one (or a few) extremely simple ancestral forms. And eventually it came to be accepted that ancestral life had not been created: it must have originated from non-living matter at some stage in our planet's history.

Nor could it be supposed that any supernatural agency was needed to guide or interfere with the detailed or general course of evolution: that too is determined by simple natural causes. The apparent purposefulness of biological mechanisms (and, we can now say, evolutionary trends) turns out not to demand conscious purpose by a Divine artificer. . . .[7]. . . .

Our new knowledge of the mechanism of heredity and variation is enlarging our ideas of the power of artificial selection to extend the work of natural selection. By radiation, we are now artificially producing mutations in crop-plants where the range of variation is low, and then selecting and recombining the few favourable ones to make new breeds. By these and other methods we are doing in a few decades what it took natural selection millions of years to effect—extending the range of species into previously prohibited habitats. . . .[8]. . . .

. . . We now realize that evolution operates in the whole of

[2] See p. 50, footnote 2.

nature, and that it can best be defined as a one-way process of change in time which in its course increases diversification, creates novelty, and raises the upper level of organization. Thus, in a certain sense, all phenomenal reality is a single process of evolution. . . .[11]. . . .

. . . The process of evolution, as represented by man, is now, for the first time in its long history, becoming conscious of itself and of its nature. Man is the latest dominant type to be produced in evolution and the only one capable of further major advance. I would prophecy that one of the major scientific enterprises of the moderately near future will be a study of human possibilities and the evolutionary implications of attempts to realize them. If so, the idea of evolution, which became scientifically respectable a bare century ago, will find its most important application in the central problem of human destiny.[12]

APPENDIX I

George Bernard Shaw (1856-1950)

From *Back to Methuselah, A Metabiological Pentateuch.* New York and London: Oxford University Press, 1947. (Published originally in 1921.) Reprinted by permission of the Public Trustee and The Society of Authors.

PREFACE: *THE INFIDEL HALF CENTURY*

The Advent of the Neo-Darwinians

. . . If Darwin had really led the world at one bound from the book of Genesis to Heredity, to Modification of Species by Selection, and to Evolution, he would have been a philosopher and a prophet as well as an eminent professional naturalist, with geology as a hobby. The delusion that he had actually achieved this feat did no harm at first, because if people's views are sound, about evolution or anything else, it does not make two straws difference whether they call the revealer of their views [viii] Tom or Dick. But later on such apparently negligible errors have awkward consequences. Darwin was given an imposing reputation as discoverer and founder of Evolution when he had really only sidetracked it by shewing that many of its developments can be accounted for by what he called Natural Selection, meaning that instead of being evolved to fulfil some vital purpose they were the aimless and promiscuous results of external material pressures and accidents leading to the survival of the fittest to survive under such circumstances. With, of course, the extinction of the unfit. Of this he gave many examples.

As the vogue of Evolution, begun by Goethe [1] and maintained by Darwin's grandfather, faded out in 1830, neither Darwin nor his contemporaries seem to have been aware of it. The next generation accepted Natural Selection as the only method of biological development, and thereby came into conflict with the old Creative Evolutionists and with Darwin himself: a schism which obliged them to distinguish themselves as Neo-Darwinians.

---

[1] See p. 46, footnote 5.

Before ten more years had elapsed, the Neo-Darwinians were dominating biological Science. It was 1906; I was fifty; I had published my own view of evolution in a play called Man and Superman; and I found that most people were unable to understand how I could be an Evolutionist and not a Neo-Darwinian, or why I derided Neo-Darwinism as a mischievous heresy, and would fall on its professors slaughterously in public discussions. . . .

Political Inadequacy of the Human Animal

Ten more years elapsed. Neo-Darwinism in politics had produced a European catastrophe of a magnitude so appalling, and a scope so unpredictable, that as I write these lines [ix] in 1920, it is still far from certain whether our civilization will survive it. . . .

Cowardice of the Irreligious

. . . At the present moment one half of Europe, having knocked the other half down, is trying to kick it to death, and may succeed: a procedure which is, logically, sound Neo-Darwinism. And the good-natured majority are looking on in helpless horror, or allowing themselves to be persuaded by the newspapers of their exploiters that the kicking is not only a sound commercial investment, but an act of divine justice of which they are the ardent instruments. . . .[x]. . . .

Flimsiness of Civilization

What hope is there . . . of human improvement? According to the Neo-Darwinists, to the Mechanists, no hope whatever, because improvement can come only through some senseless accident which must, on the statistical average of accidents, be presently wiped out by some other equally senseless accident. . . .[xv]. . . .

Voluntary Longevity

. . . [August] Weismann, a very clever and suggestive biologist who was unhappily stultified by Neo-Darwinism, pointed out that as certain living organisms, though they multiply by splitting into living halves, never die, death is neither natural nor inevitable. . . .[xvi]

Here, then, is an alternative to the scrapping of our species as a political failure, and its replacement by a new experiment in creative evolution. And so, to make the suggestion more entertaining than it would be to most people in the form of a biological treatise, I have written Back to Methuselah as a contribution to the modern Bible.

. . . I must give here a little history of the conflict between the view of Evolution taken by the Darwinians (though not altogether by Darwin himself) and called Natural Selection, and that which is emerging, under the title of Creative Evolution, as the genuinely scientific religion for which all wise men are now anxiously looking. . . .[xvii]. . . .

Corrected Dates for the Discovery of Evolution

From 1830 to 1859, when Darwin published his Origin of Species, there was a slump in Evolutionism. Nobody who knew the theory was adding anything to it. This slump not only heightened the general impression of entire novelty when Darwin brought the subject to the front again but prevented him from realizing how much had been done before, even by his own grandfather, to whom he was accused of being unjust. His insistence on the godless part played in organic development by circumstances delighted the sceptical intelligentsia. Nowadays, when we are turning in weary disgust and disillusion from Neo-Darwinism and Mechanism to Vitalism and Creative Evolution, it is difficult to credit this. . . .[xxviii]. . . .

The Moment and the Man

[The] superstition of a continual capricious disorder in nature, of a lawgiver who was also a lawbreaker, made atheists in all directions among clever and light-minded people. But atheism did not account for Paley's watch.[2] Atheism accounted for nothing; and it was the business of science to account for everything that was plainly accountable. Science had no use for mere negation: what was desired by it above all things just then was a demonstration that the evidences of design could be explained without resort to the hypothesis of a personal designer. If only some genius, whilst admitting Paley's facts, could knock the brains out of Paley by the discovery of a method whereby watches could happen without watchmakers, that genius was assured of such a welcome from the thought of his day as no natural philosopher had ever enjoyed before.

The time being thus ripe, the genius appeared; and his name was Charles Darwin. And now, what did Darwin really discover? . . . [xxxv]. . . .

. . . The Darwinian process may be described as a chapter of accidents. As such, it seems simple, because you do not at first realize all that it involves. But when its whole significance dawns on you, your heart sinks into a heap of sand within you. There is a hideous fatalism about it, a ghastly and damnable reduction of beauty and intelligence, of strength and purpose, of honor and aspiration, to such casually picturesque changes as an avalanche may make in a mountain landscape, or a railway accident in a human figure. To call this Natural Selection is a blasphemy, possible to many for whom Nature is nothing but a casual aggregation of inert and dead matter, but eternally impossible to the spirits and souls of the righteous. If it be

---

[2] William Paley (see p. 99, footnote 3) constructed a popular analogy to demonstrate the existence of God: just as the existence of a watch argues for a master watchmaker, so the existence of the ordered, complex universe, including man, argues for a master creator or designer, i.e., God.

no blasphemy, but a truth of science, then the stars of heaven, the showers and dew, the winter and summer, the fire and heat, the mountains and hills, may no longer be called to exalt the Lord with us by praise: their work is to modify all things by blindly starving and murdering everything that is not lucky enough to survive in the universal struggle for hogwash. . . .[xxxvii] . . .

The Brink of the Bottomless Pit

. . . We had been so oppressed by the notion that everything that happened in the world was the arbitrary personal act of an arbitrary personal god of dangerously jealous and cruel personal character, so that even the relief of the pains of childbed and the operating table by chloroform was objected to as an interference with his arrangements which he would probably resent, that we just jumped at Darwin. When Napoleon was asked what would happen when he died, he said that Europe would express its intense relief with a great 'Ouf!' Well, when Darwin killed the god who objected to chloroform,[xxxviii] everybody who had ever thought about it said 'Ouf!' Paley was buried fathoms deep with his watch, now fully accounted for without any divine artificer at all. We were so glad to be rid of both that we never gave a thought to the consequences. . . . In 1906 I might have vituperated Jehovah more heartily than ever Shelley [3] did without eliciting a protest in any circle of thinkers, or shocking any public audience accustomed to modern discussion; but when I described Darwin as 'an intelligent and industrious pigeon fancier,' that blasphemous levity, as it seemed, was received with horror and indignation. The tide has now turned; and every puny whipster may say what he likes about Darwin; but anyone who wants to know what it was to be a Lamarckian during the last quarter of the nineteenth century has only to read Mr. Festing Jones's memoir of Samuel Butler [4] to learn how completely even a man of genius could isolate himself by antagonizing Darwin on the one hand and the Church on the other.

Why Darwin Converted the Crowd

I am well aware that in describing the effect of Darwin's discovery on naturalists and on persons capable of serious reflection on the nature and attributes of God, I am leaving the vast mass of the British public out of account. I have pointed out elsewhere that the British nation does not consist [xxxix] of atheists and Plymouth Brothers; and I am not now going to pretend that it ever consisted of Darwinians and Lamarckians. The average citizen is irreligious and unscientific; you talk to him about cricket and gold, market prices and party politics,

---

[3] Percy Bysshe Shelley (1798-1822), English poet.

[4] Henry Festing Jones (1851-1928), *Samuel Butler, Author of Erewhon (1835-1902)-A Memoir* (London: Macmillan and Co., 1919).

not about evolution and relativity, transubstantiation and predestination. Nothing will knock into his head the fateful distinction between Evolution as promulgated by Erasmus Darwin, and Circumstantial (so-called Natural) Selection as revealed by his grandson. Yet the doctrine of Charles reached him, though the doctrine of Erasmus had passed over his head. Why did not Erasmus Darwin popularize the word Evolution as effectively as Charles?

The reason was, I think, that Circumstantial Selection is easier to understand, more visible and concrete, than Lamarckian evolution. Evolution as a philosophy and physiology of the will is a mystical process, which can be apprehended only by a trained, apt, and comprehensive thinker. . . . But pigeon fanciers, dog fanciers, gardeners, stock breeders, or stud grooms, can understand Circumstantial Selection, because it is their business to produce transformation by imposing on flowers and animals a Selection From Without. All that Darwin had to say to them was that the mere chapter of accidents is always doing on a huge scale what they themselves are doing on a very small scale. . . .[xl]. . . . Now if you are familiar with these three processes: the survival of the fittest, sexual selection, and variation leading to new kinds, there is nothing to puzzle you in Darwinism.

That was the secret of Darwin's popularity. He never puzzled anybody. If very few of us have read The Origin of Species from end to end, it is not because it overtaxes our mind, but because we take in the whole case and are prepared to accept it long before we have come to the end of the innumerable instances and illustrations of which the book mainly consists. . . . Darwin's industry was enormous. His patience, his perseverance, his conscientiousness reached the human limit. But he never got deeper beneath or higher above his facts than an ordinary man could follow him. He was not conscious of having raised a stupendous issue, because, though it arose instantly, it was not his business. He was conscious of having discovered a process of transformation and modification which accounted for a great deal of natural history. But he did not put it forward as accounting for the whole of natural history. He included it under the heading of Evolution, though it was only pseudo-evolution at best, but he revealed it as *a* method of evolution, not as *the* method of evolution. He did not pretend that it excluded other methods, or that it was the chief method. Though he demonstrated that many transformations which had been taken as functional [xli] adaptations (the current phrase for Lamarckian evolution) either certainly were or conceivably might be due to Circumstantial Selection, he was careful not to claim that he had superseded Lamarck or disproved Functional Adaptation. In short, he was not a Darwinian, but an honest naturalist working away at his job with so little preoccupation with theological speculation that he never quarrelled with the theistic Unitarianism into which he was born, and remained to the end the engagingly simple and socially easy-going soul he had been in his boyhood, when his elders doubted whether he would ever be of much use in the world.

How We Rushed down a Steep Place

Not so the rest of us intellectuals. We all began going to the devil with the utmost cheerfulness. Everyone who had a mind to change, changed it. Only Samuel Butler . . . reacted against him furiously; ran up the Lamarckian flag to the top-gallant peak; declared with penetrating accuracy that Darwin had 'banished mind from the universe'; and even attacked Darwin's personal character, unable to bear the fact that the author of so abhorrent a doctrine was an amiable and upright man. Nobody would listen to him. He was so completely submerged by the flowing tide of Darwinism that when Darwin wanted to clear up the misunderstanding on which Butler was basing his personal attacks, Darwin's friends, very foolishly and snobbishly, persuaded him that Butler was too ill-conditioned and negligible to be answered. That they could not recognize in Butler a man of genius mattered little: what did matter was that they could not understand the provocation under which he was raging. They actually regarded the banishment of mind from the universe as a glorious enlightenment and emancipation for which he was ignorantly ungrateful. . . .[xlii] . . . . We were intellectually intoxicated with the idea that the world could make itself without design, purpose, skill, or intelligence: in short, without life. . . . We took a perverse pleasure in arguing, without the least suspicion that we were reducing ourselves to absurdity, that all the books in the British Museum library might have been written word for word as they stand on the shelves if no human being had ever been conscious, just as the trees stand in the forest doing wonderful things without consciousness.

And the Darwinians went far beyond denying consciousness to trees. Weismann insisted that the chick breaks out of its eggshell automatically; that the butterfly, springing into the air to avoid the pounce of the lizard, 'does not wish to avoid death; knows nothing about death,' what has happened being simply that a flight instinct evolved by Circumstantial Selection reacts promptly to a visual impression produced by the lizard's movement. . . .[xliii] . . . .

Darwinism Not Finally Refutable

. . . When a man tells you that you are a product of Circumstantial Selection solely, you cannot finally disprove it. You can only tell him out of the depths of your inner conviction that he is a fool and a liar. But as this, though British, is uncivil, it is wiser to offer him the counter-assurance that you are the product of Lamarckian evolution, formerly called Functional Adaptation and now Creative Evolution, and challenge him to disprove *that*, which he can no more do than you can disprove Circumstantial Selection, both forces being conceivably able to produce anything if you only give them rope enough. . . .[xlv]. . . .

Why Darwin Pleased the Socialists

The Humanitarians were not alone among the agitators in their welcome to Darwin. He had the luck to please everybody who had an axe to grind. The Militarists were as enthusiastic as the Humanitarians, the Socialists as the Capitalists. . . .[li]. . . .

The Poetry and Purity of Materialism

Thus the stars in their courses fought for Darwin. Every faction drew a moral from him; every catholic hater of faction founded a hope on him; every blackguard felt justified by him; and every saint felt encouraged by him. The notion that any harm could come of so splendid an enlightenment seemed as silly as the notion that the atheists would steal all our spoons. . . .[lvi]. . . .

Political Opportunism in Excelsis [5]

The moment . . . [God] was slain by Darwin, Public Opinion, as divine deputy, lost its sanctity. Politicians no longer told themselves that the British public would never suffer this or that: they allowed themselves to know that for their own personal purposes, which are limited to their ten or twenty years on the front benches in parliament, the British Public can be humbugged and coerced into believing and suffering everything that it pays their rulers to impose on them, and that any excuse for an unpopular step will serve if it can be kept in countenance for three days: that is, until the terms of the excuse are forgotten. With its last ideal gone, policy died and was succeeded by unprincipled opportunism. All Governments became like the tramp who walks always with the wind and ends as a pauper, or the stone that rolls down the hill and ends as an avalanche: their way was the way to destruction.

The Betrayal of Western Civilization

Within sixty years from the publication of Darwin's Origin of Species political opportunism had brought parliaments into contempt; created a popular demand for direct action by the organized industries ('Syndicalism'); and wrecked the centre of Europe in a paroxysm of that chronic terror of one another, that cowardice of the irreligious, which, masked in [lix] the bravado of militarist patriotism, had ridden the Powers like a nightmare since the Franco-Prussian war of 1870-71. . . .

In 1918 the surrender of Germany on terms which the victors never dreamt of observing did not change the situation.[lx] If the

---

[5] In the highest degree.

Western Powers had selected their allies in the Lamarckian manner intelligently, purposely, and vitally, *ad majorem Dei gloriam*,[6] as good Europeans, there would have been a durable League of Nations and no war. But because the selection relied on was purely circumstantial opportunist selection, so that the alliances were mere marriages of convenience, they have turned out, not merely as badly as might have been expected, but far worse than the blackest pessimist had ever imagined possible. How it will all end we do not yet know. When wolves combine to kill a horse, the death of the horse only sets them fighting one another for the choicest morsels. . . .[lxi]. . . .

The Religious Art of the Twentieth Century

Creative Evolution is already a religion, and is indeed now unmistakably the religion of the twentieth century, newly arisen from the ashes of pseudo-Christianity, or mere scepticism, and of the soulless affirmations and blind negations of the Mechanists and Neo-Darwinians. But it cannot become a popular religion until it has its legends, its parables, its miracles. And when I say popular I do not mean apprehensible by villagers only. I mean apprehensible by Cabinet Ministers as well. It is unreasonable to look to the professional politician and administrator for light and leading in religion. He is neither a philosopher nor a prophet: if he were, he would be philosophizing and prophesying, and not neglecting both for the drudgery of practical government. . . .[lxviii]. . . .

---

[6] For the greater glory of God.

APPENDIX II

A Folk Epic of Evolution on Trial: The Scopes Trial of 1925

Tennessee's Butler Act,[1] or anti-evolution law, was passed by the state legislature on March 13, 1925. John T. Scopes, a science instructor in the Rhea County Central High School, believing that he could not teach from the official biology text without at the same time teaching the fact of organic evolution and thus violating the law, agreed to become the central figure in the first legal test of the Act. It was therefore arranged for him publicly to "teach evolution," and he was arrested on May 5.

The Scopes Trial was held in Dayton from July 10 to 21, 1925. The presiding judge was John T. Raulston, and the lawyers arguing the case included Attorney-General A. T. Stewart of Tennessee and William Jennings Bryan for the state and Clarence Darrow and Dudley Field Malone for the defense. The state's charge was simple and direct: it contended that Scopes had in fact violated the Butler Act, and it called witnesses to testify to that effect. The defense did not deny the charge, but it maintained that in teaching as he had, Scopes had not necessarily violated the Bible, properly interpreted. Its strategy was to summon a number of distinguished scientists for "experts' testimony" to the validity and

---

[1] Sponsored by John Washington Butler.

147

respectability of the theory of evolution. However, after hearing arguments by both sides, Judge Raulston ruled against the admission of such testimony. The defense now had no alternative but to ask the jury for a unanimous verdict of guilty, so that it could appeal to the state supreme court. On July 21, Scopes was found guilty and fined $100.

The trial contained, among other things, a highly dramatic contest between Bryan, three times Democratic candidate for the presidency of the United States but now past his prime (he died a few days after the end of the trial), and Darrow, America's greatest defense lawyer, fresh from his triumph in the Loeb-Leopold case in Chicago a year earlier. Darrow's devastating questioning of Bryan on the witness stand (in a clever maneuver, the defense called him to testify as a "Bible expert") served as a sensational climax to a legal proceeding that was followed with great interest throughout the country as well as abroad.

Scopes appealed his conviction to the Tennessee Supreme Court, but on January 15, 1927, that court upheld the Butler Act and rejected the defense motion for a new hearing. Citing a legal technicality, it further asked that a *nolle prosequi* [2] be entered. Thus the case was thrown out of the courts altogether, rendering impossible any further appeal.

---

[2] Literally, "to be unwilling to prosecute"—a legal term indicating that the state officially refuses to pursue its case.

From *The World's Most Famous Court Trial
—Tennessee Evolution Case.* 3rd ed. Cincin-
nati: National Book Co., 1925.

I—*THE BUTLER ACT*

Section 1. Be it enacted by the general assembly of the state of
Tennessee, that it shall be unlawful for any teacher in any of the universities, normals, and all other public schools of the state, which are
supported in whole or in part by the public school funds of the state,
to teach any theory that denies the story of the Divine creation of
man as taught in the Bible, and to teach instead that man has descended from a lower order of animals.[112]

Section 2. Be it further enacted that any teacher found guilty
of a violation of this act shall be guilty of a misdemeanor and upon
conviction shall be fined not less than $100, nor more than $500, for
each offense.3 [113]

II—*INDICTMENT*

State of Tennessee,
County of Rhea.

Circuit Court,
July Special Term, 1925.

The grand jurors for the state aforesaid, being duly summoned,
elected, empaneled, sworn, and charged to inquire for the body of the
county aforesaid, upon their oaths present:

That John Thomas Scopes, heretofore on the 24th day of April,
1925, in the county aforesaid, then and there, unlawfully did wilfully
teach in the public schools of Rhea county, Tennessee, which said
public schools are supported in part and in whole by the public school
fund of the state, a certain theory and theories that deny the story
of the divine creation of man as taught in the Bible, and did teach
instead thereof that man was descended from a lower order of animals,
he, the said John Thomas Scopes, being at the time, or prior thereto,
a teacher in the public schools of Rhea county, Tennessee, aforesaid,
against the peace and dignity of the state.

A. T. Stewart,
Attorney-General [47]

III—*OPENING ADDRESS FOR THE DEFENSE BY DUDLEY FIELD MALONE*

. . . We maintain that since the Defendant Scopes has been in-
dicted under a statute which prohibits the teaching of the evolutionary

---

3 A third section of the statute, not contained in the source, specifies that the
act should take effect "from and after its passage, the public welfare requiring it."

theory, the prosecution must prove as part of its case what evolution is.

So that there shall be no misunderstanding and that no one shall be able to misinterpret our position we wish to state at the beginning of the case that the defense believes there is a direct conflict between the theory of evolution and the theories of creation as set forth in the Book of Genesis.

Neither do we believe that the stories of creation as set forth in the Bible are reconcilable or scientifically correct. . . . We shall make it perfectly clear that . . . there are millions of people who believe in evolution and in the stories of creation as set forth in the Bible and who find no conflict between the two. The defense maintains that this is a matter of faith and interpretation, which each individual must determine for himself, and if you, men of the jury, are able to reconcile the theory of evolution and the theories of creation as set forth in the Bible, you are not only entitled to your view, but you will be supported in it by millions of your citizens who are of high culture, learning and deep religious faith. . . .

While the defense thinks there is a conflict between evolution and the Old Testament, we believe there is no conflict between evolution and Christianity. There may be a conflict between evolution and the peculiar ideas of Christianity, which are held by Mr. Bryan as the evangelical leader of the prosecution, but we deny that the evangelical leader of the prosecution is an authorized spokesman for the Christians of the United States. . . .[113] . . .

. . . We shall prove by experts and scientists in every field of scientific knowledge that there is no branch of science which can be taught today without teaching the theory of evolution, and that this applies to geology, biology, botany, astronomy, medicine, chemistry, bacteriology, embryology, zoology, sanitation, forestry and agriculture. We will show that it will have been impossible for men like Luther Burbank and others without knowledge and faith in the theory of evolution to produce their invaluable experiments and results.

The prosecution has twice since the beginning of the trial referred to man as descended from monkeys. This may be the understanding of the theory of evolution of the prosecution. It is not the view, opinion or knowledge of evolution held by the defense. No scientist of any pre-eminent standing today holds such a view. The most that science says today is that there is an order of men like mamals [sic] which are more capable of walking erect than other animals, and more capable than other animals in the use of the forefeet as hands. . . .[115] . . .

The defense denies that it is part of any movement or conspiracy on the part of scientists to destroy the authority of Christianity or the Bible. The defense denies that any such conspiracy exists except in the mind and purposes of the evangelical leader of the prosecution.

The defense maintains that the book of Genesis is in part a hymn, in part an allegory and a work of religious interpretations written by men who believed that the earth was flat and whose authority cannot be accepted to control the teachings of science in our schools. . . .[116]

IV—*SPEECH BY WILLIAM JENNINGS BRYAN AGAINST PERMITTING EXPERTS' TESTIMONY ON BEHALF OF THE DEFENSE*

. . . The question is can a minority in this state come in and compel a teacher to teach that the Bible is not true and make the parents of these children pay the expenses of a teacher to tell their children what these people believe is false and dangerous? Has it come to a time when the minority can take charge of a state like Tennessee and compel the majority to pay their teachers while they take religion out of the heart of the children of the parents who pay the teachers? . . .[172] . . .

On page 194 [of George Hunter's *A Civic Biology,* from which Scopes taught] we have a diagram, and this diagram purports to give some one's family tree. Not only his ancestors but his collateral relatives. We are told just how many animal species there are, 518,900. And in this diagram, beginning with protozoa we have the animals classified. We have circles differing in size according to the number of species in them and we have a guess that they give. . . .

. . . And then we have mammals, 3,500, and there is a little circle and man is in the circle, find him, find man.[174]

There is that book! There is the book they were teaching your children that man was a mammal and so indistinguishable among the mammals that they leave him there with thirty-four hundred and ninety-nine other mammals. . . .

I will give you the family tree according to Darwin. If we are going to have family trees here, let us have something that is reliable. I will give you the only family tree that any believer in evolution has ever dared to outline—no other family tree that any evolutionist has ever proposed, has as many believers as Darwin has in his family tree. Some of them have discarded his explanations. Natural selections! People confuse evolution with Darwinism. They did not use to complain. It was not until Darwin was brought out into the open, it was not until the absurdities of Darwin had made his explanations the laughing stock, that they began to try to distinguish between Darwinism and evolution. They explained that evolutionists had discarded Darwin's idea of sexual selection—I should think they would discard it, and they are discarding the doctrine of natural selection.

But, my friends, when they discard his explanations, they still teach his doctrines. Not one of these evolutionists has discarded Darwin's doctrine that makes life begin with one cell in the sea and continue in one unbroken line to man. Not one of them has discarded that. . . .[175] . . .

. . . Evolution is not a theory, but a hypothesis. Huxley said it could not raise to the dignity of a theory until they found some species that had developed according to the hypothesis, and at that time, Huxley's time, there had never been found a single species, the origin of which could be traced to another species. Darwin himself said he thought it was strange that with two or three million species they had not been able to find one that they could trace to another. . . .[177] . . .

. . . We have a book here [the Bible] that shows everything that is needed to make one understand evolution, and to show that the man violated the law. Then why should we prolong this case? We can bring our experts here for the Christians; for every one they can bring who does not believe in Christianity, we can bring more than one who believes in the Bible and rejects evolution, and our witnesses will be just as good experts as theirs on a question of that kind. We could have a thousand or a million witnesses, but this case as to whether evolution is true or not, is not going to be tried here, within this city; if it is carried to the state's courts, it will not be tried there, and if it is taken to the great court at Washington, it will not be tried there. No, my friends, no court or the law, and no jury, great or small, is going to destroy the issue between the believer and the unbeliever. The Bible is the Word of God, the Bible is the only expression of man's hope of salvation. The Bible, the record of the Son of God, the Savior of the world, born of the virgin Mary, crucified and risen again. That Bible is not going to be driven out of this court [181] by experts who come hundreds of miles to testify that they can reconcile evolution, with its ancestor in the jungle, with man made by God in His image, and put here for purposes as a part of the divine plan. No, we are not going to settle that question here, and I think we ought to confine ourselves to the law and to the evidence that can be admitted in accordance with the law. . . .[182]

V—SPEECH BY DUDLEY FIELD MALONE IN FAVOR OF PERMITTING EXPERTS' TESTIMONY ON BEHALF OF THE DEFENSE

There is never a duel with the truth. The truth always wins and we are not afraid of it. The truth is no coward. The truth does not need the law. The truth does not need the forces of government. The truth does not need Mr. Bryan. The truth is imperishable, eternal and immortal and needs no human agency to support it. We are ready to tell the truth as we understand [187] it and we do not fear all the truth they can present as facts. We are ready. We are ready. We feel we stand with progress. We feel we stand with science. We feel we stand with intelligence. We feel we stand with fundamental freedom in America. We are not afraid. Where is the fear? We meet it, where is the fear? We defy it, we ask your honor to admit the evidence as a matter of correct law, as a matter of sound procedure and as a matter of justice to the defense in this case. (Profound and continued applause.) . . .[188]

VI–*INTERROGATION OF WILLIAM JENNINGS BRYAN BY CLARENCE DARROW*

Q—Do you claim that everything in the Bible should be literally interpreted?

A—I believe everything in the Bible should be accepted as it is given there; some of the Bible is given illustratively. For instance: "Ye are the salt of the earth." I would not insist that man was actually salt, or that he had flesh of salt, but it is used in the sense of salt as saying God's people. . . .

Q—Do you consider the story of Jonah and the whale a miracle?

A—I think it is.

Q—Do you believe Joshua made the sun stand still? [285]

A—I believe what the Bible says. I suppose you mean that the earth stood still?

Q—I don't know. I am talking about the Bible now.

A—I accept the Bible absolutely.

Q—The Bible says that Joshua commanded the sun to stand still for the purpose of lengthening the day, doesn't it, and you believe it?

A—I do. . . .[286]. . . .

Q—Now, Mr. Bryan, have you ever pondered what would have happened to the earth if it had stood still?

A—No.

Q—You have not?

A—No; the God I believe in could have taken care of that, Mr. Darrow. . . .[287]. . . .

The Witness—These gentlemen have not had much chance—they did not come here to try this case. They came here to try revealed religion. I am here to defend it, and they can ask me any question they please.

The Court—All right.

(Applause from the court yard.)

Darrow—Great applause from the bleachers.

Bryan—From those whom you call "yokels."

Darrow—I have never called them yokels.

Bryan—That is the ignorance of Tennessee, the bigotry.

Darrow—You mean who are applauding you? (Applause.)

Bryan—Those are the people whom you insult.

Darrow—You insult every man of science and learning in the world because he does not believe in your fool religion. . . .[288]. . . .

Q—Mr. Bryan, could you tell me how old the earth is?

A—No, sir, I couldn't.

Q—Could you come anywhere near it?

A—I wouldn't attempt to. I could possibly come as near as the scientists do, but I had rather be more accurate before I give a guess.

Q—You don't think much of scientists, do you?

A—Yes, sir, I do, sir. . . .[296] . . .

Q—Do you think the earth was made in six days? [298]

A—Not six days of twenty-four hours.

Q—Doesn't it say so?

A—No, sir.

Gen. Stewart—I want to interpose another objection. What is the purpose of this examination?

Bryan—The purpose is to cast ridicule on everybody who believes in the Bible, and I am perfectly willing that the world shall know that these gentlemen have no other purpose than ridiculing every Christian who believes in the Bible.

Darrow—We have the purpose of preventing bigots and ignoramuses from controlling the education of the United States and you know it, and that is all.

Bryan—I am glad to bring out that statement. I want the world to know that this evidence is not for the view Mr. Darrow and his associates have filed affidavits here stating, the purposes of which I understand it, is to show that the Bible story is not true.

Malone—Mr. Bryan seems anxious to get some evidence in the record that would tend to show that those affidavits are not true.

Bryan—I am not trying to get anything into the record. I am simply trying to protect the word of God against the greatest atheist or agnostic in the United States. (Prolonged applause.) I want the papers to know that I am not afraid to get on the stand in front of him and let him do his worst. I want the world to know. (Prolonged applause.) . . .[299] . . .

Q—Now, you refer to the cloud that was put in the heaven after the flood, the rainbow. Do you believe in that?

A—Read it.

Q—All right, Mr. Bryan, I will read it for you.

Bryan—Your honor, I think I can shorten this testimony. The only purpose Mr. Darrow has is to slur at the Bible, but I will answer his question. I will answer it all at once, and I have no objection in the world, I want the world to know that this man, who does not believe in a God, is trying to use a court in Tennessee—

Darrow—I object to that.

Bryan (continuing)—to slur at it, and while it will require time, I am willing to take it.

Darrow—I object to your statement. I am exempting you on your fool ideas that no intelligent Christian on earth believes. . . .[304]

To this day, Tennessee's Butler Act remains in the state's statutes unrepealed, though it is not enforced and has never again been tested in the courts. Interest in the Scopes Trial has recently been revived by the production of the American play *Inherit the Wind,* by Jerome Lawrence and Robert E. Lee (published in 1955 by Random House), which was based on the events and principals of the trial. A motion picture version of this play is being produced in Hollywood. A brief but complete history of the trial has also appeared recently: Ray Ginger's *Six Days or Forever? Tennessee v. John Thomas Scopes* (Boston: Beacon Press, 1958).

QUESTIONS AND TOPICS FOR RESEARCH PAPERS

Part One: The Sources of the Darwinian Revolution

Questions:

1. Trace briefly the history of the concurrent formulations of the theory of natural selection by Darwin and Wallace, as explained by Lyell and Hooker in the Linnean Society Papers and by Darwin himself in *The Origin of Species.*

2. Compare or contrast Darwin's contributions to the Linnean Society Papers with the selections from *The Origin of Species.* What additional information or explanation does Darwin supply in the 1859 work, and how does it help you understand natural selection? Does Darwin's letter to Asa Gray add to your understanding, and if so, how?

3. State briefly but precisely Darwin's conception of "descent with modification" of organic beings. What kinds of evidence does he offer in favor of organic evolution? How does he support his contention that living beings "seem to me to become ennobled" when accounted for in terms of the theory of evolution?

4. Describe the essential similarities and differences between Darwin's and Wallace's conceptions of natural selection. In particular, how does each man use the following terms, if he uses them at all: "survival of the fittest," "struggle for existence," "variety," "variation," "species," "selection," and "natural selection"?

5. What was Darwin's purpose in writing *The Descent of Man?* What is the essential connection between the views expressed in this book and those expressed in *The Origin of Species?* Explain Darwin's conception of "sexual selection" and its relationship to his analysis of the process of evolution.

Topics for Short Research Papers:

1. A Brief Account of the Formulations of the Theory of Natural Selection by Charles Darwin and Alfred Russel Wallace

2. The Leading Principles of Darwinism, as Contained in Darwin's *The Origin of Species* and *The Descent of Man*

3. Darwin and Wallace: A Brief Analysis of Their Conceptions of Natural Selection

4. Darwin's Arguments in Favor of Organic Evolution

5. Darwin's Explanation of the Origin of Man

157

Part Two: Early Defenders of Darwinism

Questions:

1. To what extent do Lyell and Hooker believe in (1) organic evolution and (2) natural selection? Which of these men seems to you to have become more completely converted to the doctrine of transmutation of species?

2. On precisely what grounds does Asa Gray maintain that natural selection and natural theology are not inconsistent? How favorably inclined is Gray toward natural selection?

3. Huxley is often represented as having given his blanket approval to Darwinism. Do the selections you have read indicate that such a representation is correct? What questions did Huxley have about Darwinian principles? What doubts, if any, did he have about the theory of organic evolution itself?

4. In what important respects does Wallace diverge from the views expressed by Darwin in *The Origin of Species* and *The Descent of Man?* In particular, what is Wallace's attitude towards the intellectual, moral, and spiritual evolution of man?

5. What are the principal arguments of Huxley and Wallace in opposition to theories of special creation and immutability and to the evolutionary doctrines of Lamarck? What, if anything, do Lyell, Hooker, and Gray have to say about these matters?

Topics for Short Research Papers:

1. The Attitudes of Darwin's Early Defenders toward the Evolutionary Principles of Lamarck and Other Precursors of Darwin
2. Darwin's Supporters and the Scientific Contest of the Century: Catastrophism vs. Uniformitarianism, Special Creation vs. Organic Evolution, Immutability vs. Mutability of Species
3. Asa Gray and T. H. Huxley on the Conflict between Religion and Science
4. The Darwinism of Alfred Russel Wallace
5. Sir Charles Lyell and Joseph D. Hooker: Converts to the Theory of Organic Evolution

Part Three: Opponents of Darwinism

Questions:

1. Compare or contrast the three anonymously published reviews of *The Origin of Species.* Is any one of them kinder to Darwin than the other two, or are they equally hostile? In which is the attack on Darwinism both religious and scientific, in which exclusively religious,

in which exclusively scientific? Which of the three is (or are) expressly anti-evolutionist as well as anti-Darwinian?

2. What are the chief arguments of the advocates of special creation represented here?

3. What are the chief arguments against natural selection advanced by the evolutionists among Darwin's opponents, and what is the nature of the theory or theories which they propose to account for organic evolution?

4. Compare the over-all effectiveness of Mivart's review of *The Descent of Man* with any one of the anonymously published reviews of *The Origin of Species*. Which seems sounder, more authoritative, more judiciously expressed, and more rhetorically convincing?

5. What is Samuel Butler's purpose in contrasting what he calls the "old" and the "new" theories of evolution?

Topics for Short Research Papers:

1. Nineteenth-Century Unfavorable Criticism of Darwin's *The Origin of Species* and *The Descent of Man*

2. The Principal Religious Objections to Darwinism

3. The Principal Scientific Objections to Darwinism

4. Alternatives to Natural Selection: The Evolutionists' Attack on Darwinism

5. Anti-Evolutionism: The Doctrine of Special Creation

Part Four: New Developments: Darwinism Modified

Questions:

1. What are the basic issues involved in the controversy between the "Neo-Darwinians" and the "Neo-Lamarckians"? What differences, if any, do you see between the Lamarckian views of Spencer and Haeckel, as they are expressed in the selections you have read?

2. What is Bateson's attitude toward Mendel's law of segregation and the concept of slight, continuous variations that is implicit in natural selection?

3. What does De Vries' mutation theory consist of, and what relationship does it have to Bateson's ideas on variation? What does De Vries mean when he insists that he is not an anti-Darwinian?

4. (a) Give an account of Morgan's conception of chromosomes and genes and of how they function in the mechanism of heredity. (b) What is Fisher's stated purpose in writing *The Genetical Theory of Natural Selection,* and why does he consider it a worthy and necessary one?

5. Explain precisely what Julian Huxley means when he says that Darwinism has now achieved a "modern synthesis." What does this synthesis consist of, and how, according to Huxley, does it determine the validity or invalidity of Darwinism in our time?

Topics for Short Research Papers:

1. Spencer vs. Weismann: "Neo-Darwinism" vs. "Neo-Lamarckism"
2. The Nature and Origin of Hugo de Vries' Mutation Theory
3. Mendel's Laws and the Mechanism of the Chromosome Theory of Heredity
4. William Bateson's Views on Variation and Heredity
5. The Validity of Darwinism in Our Time

Questions on the Entire Text:

1. Trace the history of Darwinism from its inception to modern times. Judging from what you have read, how would you account for its changing fortunes in the hundred years since the publication of *The Origin of Species?*

2. Explain precisely the distinctions among Darwinism (in both its general and specific senses), Lamarckism, and organic evolution.

3. Whose arguments do you consider more rhetorically effective, those of Darwin's opponents or those of his defenders? Which single attack or defense strikes you as most convincing, and why?

4. From what you have read in this book, what do you feel the resolution has been—if indeed there has been one—between religion and science on the subject of organic evolution? Would you consider a belief in Genesis and a belief in *The Origin of Species* to be incompatible?

5. Which of the "new developments" discussed in the second section of Part Four of this book seems to you to be the most significant? From what you have read here, do you feel that this development essentially supports or weakens Darwin's conception of natural selection?

6. Spencer, Gray, Wallace, Haeckel, De Vries, and Weismann all lay claim to being "Darwinians." What is the nature and extent of the Darwinism of each, and which man in your opinion expresses views most similar to those of Darwin?

7. Various opponents and defenders of Darwin, as well as Darwin himself, refer to Erasmus Darwin, Lamarck, and other naturalists whose works appeared before 1859. From these references, construct a summary statement of Darwin's debt to his precursors.

8. Discuss the significance of the distinctions between the "blending" and the "particulate" conceptions of inheritance and between the "continuous" and "discontinuous" conceptions of variation. How important has each of these distinctions been in the history of evolution and of Darwinism from 1859 to the present?

9. What, essentially, is Shaw's attitude toward evolution and natural selection? Why is he so interested in applying Darwinism to the social and political scene, and what conclusions does he reach as

the result of this application? With which of Darwin's opponents does he seem to ally himself most particularly?

10. Compare Bryan's remarks in the Scopes Trial with one or more of the attacks on either Darwinism or evolution, or both, included in Part Three of this book. In what ways are Bryan's views different, and how do you account for the differences?

Topics for Long Research Papers Based on the Entire Text:

1. A Brief History of Darwinism from 1859 to 1959
2. One Hundred Years of the Theory of Organic Evolution: 1859-1959
3. Huxley vs. the Special Creationists: The Scientific Battle of the Half-Century
4. Darwin and His Predecessors: A Summary Statement
5. Darwin, Wallace, and Weismann—Three Conceptions of Darwinism
6. Darwinism and Lamarckism: Their Leading Principles and Spokesmen
7. An Analysis of the Rhetoric and Logic of the Evolutionary Writings of Charles Darwin (or of any other single author represented in this book)
8. The Roles of Religion and Science in the Controversy over Evolution from 1859 to 1959
9. The Influence of Gregor Mendel on the Development of Theories of Heredity from 1900 to the Present Day
10. The Social and Political Implications of Theories of Evolution and of Natural Selection

SUGGESTIONS FOR FURTHER STUDY

The literature on Darwinism and organic evolution is so enormous that no collection of readings such as the present one can claim to be in any sense exhaustive. Indeed, a multi-volume encyclopedia would be required to contain all the important writing on these subjects. Nevertheless, the student must begin somewhere, and if *Darwin and His Critics* has served as his introduction to one of the most significant and pervasive of man's intellectual accomplishments, it can now also suggest to him areas for further reading and study.

I—*Organic Evolution and Biological Darwinism*

The student may wish first to explore the general field of evolutionary thought and its effect on the science of biology. One excellent modern textbook that enables him to do this is *Life: An Introduction to Biology*, by George G. Simpson, Colin S. Pittendrigh, and Lewis H. Tiffany (New York: Harcourt, Brace & Co., 1957). Among many general studies, the following are eminently readable and enlightening: *Man, Time, and Fossils: The Story of Evolution*, by Ruth Moore (New York: Alfred A. Knopf, Inc., 1953); *Darwin's Century: Evolution and the Men Who Discovered It*, by Loren Eiseley (Garden City, New York: Doubleday & Co., 1958); *Apes, Angels and Victorians*, by William Irvine (New York: McGraw-Hill Book Co., 1955); and *Darwin and the Darwinian Revolution*, by Gertrude Himmelfarb (New York: Doubleday & Company, Inc., 1959).

In recent years—and particularly during the centennial year of 1959—a number of collections of essays have been published which deal with various aspects of Darwinism and evolution. Two such books may be singled out here. *A Century of Darwin*, edited by S. A. Barnett (London: William Heinemann, Ltd., 1958), contains excellent studies by eminent contemporary scientists. *Forerunners of Darwinism: 1745-1859*, edited by Bentley Glass, Oswei Temkin, and William Strauss, Jr. (Baltimore: The Johns Hopkins Press, 1959), consists of essays by leading biologists on Darwin's precursors. In addition, *Life* magazine has recently completed a distinguished series of feature articles devoted to Darwin, Darwinism, and evolution (June 30, September 8, November 3—1958; January 26, March 16, June 1, July 20, October 19—1959); and literary journals like *Victorian Studies* (September, 1959) and *The Antioch Review* (Spring, 1959) have published centennial numbers containing essays on various aspects of the subject.

The student interested in examining the life of Darwin himself may well begin with the first third of *Darwin, Marx, Wagner*, by Jacques Barzun (Garden City, New York: Doubleday & Co., Inc., 1958 [published originally in 1941]), pp. 25-126, entitled "The Biological Revolution," a lucid and penetrating summary of the man and his work. The indispensable Darwin biography remains *The Life and Letters of Charles Darwin*, by Francis Darwin (New York: D. Appleton and Co., 1888). Darwin's widely read *Autobiography*, originally part of *The Life and Letters*, has only recently appeared for the first time in its complete version, edited by his granddaughter, Nora Barlow (London: Collins, 1958). A paperbound *Autobiography and Selected Letters*, edited by Francis Darwin, is also available (New York: Dover Publications, Inc., 1959). In addition, the student may be interested in looking at some of Darwin's other major works: *The Variation of Animals and Plants under Domestication* (1868), *The Expression of the Emotions in Man and Animals* (1872), and *The Formation of Vegetable Mould through the Action of Worms* (1881). A convenient modern anthology of Darwin's writings is *The Darwin Reader*, edited by Marston Bates and Philip S. Humphrey (New York: Charles Scribner's Sons, 1956).

For the reader who wishes to investigate the lives and accomplishments of Darwin's three great friends and supporters, there are available definitive two-volume studies of each: *Life and Letters of Thomas Henry Huxley*, by Leonard Huxley (London: Macmillan & Co., Ltd., 1900); *Life and Letters of Sir Joseph Dalton Hooker*, by Leonard Huxley (London: John Murray, 1918); and *Life, Letters, and Journals of Sir Charles Lyell*, by Mrs. Lyell, his sister-in-law (London: John Murray, 1881).

Books by writers represented in *Darwin and His Critics* in addition to those from which selections have been made include the following: Ernst Haeckel's *The Evolution of Man* (New York: D. Appleton & Co., 1887) and *The History of Creation* (New York: D. Appleton & Co., 1887); August Weismann's *The Germ-Plasm* (New York: Charles Scribner's Sons, 1893) and *The Evolution Theory* (London: Edward Arnold, 1904); *Mendel's Principles of Heredity*, by William Bateson (Cambridge: Cambridge University Press, 1913); and *Darwin and After Darwin*, by George J. Romanes (Chicago: The Open Court Publishing Co., 1892). Of the important scientists not included in this book, students may wish to read the works of Sir Francis Galton, the founder of eugenics, Gregor Mendel (whose original 1866 paper on heredity is reprinted in the Bateson volume listed above), and a host of early twentieth-century and contemporary geneticists whose important writings are too numerous to itemize in such a short space: J. B. S. Haldane, E. R. Lankester, H. J. Muller, A. H. Sturtevant, Karl Correns, Erich von Tschermak-Seysenegg, are only a few.

II—*Social Darwinism*

The chief principles of evolution and natural selection—particularly the catch-phrases of "struggle for existence" and "survival of the fittest"—very soon came to be felt in fields other than the strictly scientific. In economics, philosophy, history, national and international politics, sociology, and anthropology, there developed a body of evolutionary thought identified as Social Darwinism. By his own account,

Darwin had taken over a leading argument of British social scientist Thomas Malthus and had applied it to biology. (Students who wish to examine Malthus' *An Essay on the Principle of Population* will find it readily available.) In turn, Herbert Spencer, a philosopher and evolutionist before and after 1859, continued to the end of the century to apply evolutionary and Darwinian precepts to philosophy and the social sciences. This he did most notably in such works as *First Principles* (New York: D. Appleton & Co., 1864), *The Study of Sociology* (New York: D. Appleton & Co., 1874), *The Principles of Sociology* (New York: D. Appleton & Co., 1876-97), and *The Principles of Ethics* (New York: D. Appleton & Co., 1895-98).

Spencer's evolutionary premises led to conservative conclusions. His works were widely and enthusiastically quoted by champions of *laissez-faire* (literally, "let do") in government in their opposition to agitation for social, political, and economic reform. Progress must be slow and unhurried, in Spencerian terms. People should be left to fend for themselves, more or less—the superior and the more fit will survive, in good Darwinian fashion. Above all, government must not interfere to control the activities of men in business, finance, and industry. Spencer's influence, which was especially strong in the United States, may be traced in Richard Hofstadter's *Social Darwinism in American Thought* (Boston: The Beacon Press, 1955 [published originally in 1944]).

For William Graham Sumner, Spencer's greatest disciple in America, the application of Darwinian principles to society revealed the bleak and competitive existence which the masses of men perforce had to endure. In works like *What Social Classes Owe to Each Other* (New York: Harper & Brothers, 1883; and Caldwell, Idaho: Caxton Printers, Ltd., 1952), *Earth-Hunger and Other Essays* (New Haven: Yale University Press, 1913), and *The Challenge of Facts and Other Essays* (New Haven: Yale University Press, 1914), he took an essentially conservative position similar to Spencer's.

But in time the rigid determinism of Spencer and Sumner came to be challenged by such men as Lester Ward, Henry George, Edward Bellamy, Chauncey Wright, Charles Peirce, William James, and John Dewey. Each of these writers attacked Spencer's views of society and in varying degrees argued for reform and increased government intervention in the affairs of men. Ward's views were expressed in a number of volumes, chiefly *Dynamic Sociology* (New York: D. Appleton & Co., 1883), *Outlines of Sociology* (New York: The Macmillan Co., 1898), and *Pure Sociology* (New York: The Macmillan Co., 1903). Henry George stated his position in *A Perplexed Philosopher* (New York: C. L. Webster & Co., 1892; and New York: Schalkenbach Foundation, 1946) and other works. Edward Bellamy wrote the utopian "novel" *Looking Backward* (Boston: Houghton Mifflin Co., 1889), in large part an attack on the Spencerian application of natural selection to society. Wright, Peirce, and particularly James developed the philosophy of Pragmatism, the latter in such works as *The Principles of Psychology* (New York: Henry Holt & Co., 1890) and *Pragmatism* (New York: Longmans, Green & Co., 1907). (Paperbound editions of both books are available.) Pragmatism denied that nature and environment and the "struggle for existence" determined absolutely the fate of men, and asserted instead that it was within man's power to better his circumstances, to adapt himself to his environment. And John Dewey, with his Instrumentalism, moved even further away from the Social Darwinism of Spencer, in books like *Reconstruction in Philosophy* (New York: Henry Holt & Co., 1920), and himself participated actively in reform movements.

Darwinism made itself felt with particular force during the past half-century in the sphere of international politics, and the interested student will profit by an examination of its relationship to Marxism—and ultimately to Soviet Communism, to Benito Mussolini and Fascism, to Adolf Hitler and Nazism, and to World Wars I and II. Karl Marx's indebtedness to *The Origin of Species* is a matter of record, expressed in a letter written to Friedrich Engels: "Darwin's book is very important and serves me as a basis in natural science for the class struggle in history." Marxists adopted Spencer's concept of "survival of the fittest," but at the same time and at the furthest remove from Spencer, preached the reverse of *laissez-faire*. Marx worked out his principles of socialism in *The Communist Manifesto* (written in collaboration with Engels in 1848) and in *Das Kapital* (Volume I published in 1867, Volumes II and III posthumously in 1885-94). Both works are available in English translation. *Mein Kampf* (written by Hitler during his imprisonment in 1924), in which the future German dictator mapped out his master-plan for world conquest, is available in English translation. Under the Nazi dictatorship the theory of a "master race" was evolved, and the pure "Aryans" assumed unqualified power over "non-Aryan" Jews, over the sick and the aged, and over other minority groups, who were then marked for systematic destruction.

III—*Darwinism and Imaginative Literature of the Nineteenth and Twentieth Centuries*

The influence of Darwinism on imaginative literature may be seen in the works of the Victorian poets in England and the naturalistic novelists in the United States in the late nineteenth and early twentieth centuries. Among studies of evolution in the poems of the great Victorians, the student will find particularly helpful Lionel Stevenson's *Darwin Among the Poets* (Chicago: University of Chicago Press, 1932) and Georg Roppen's *Evolution and Poetic Belief* (Oslo: Oslo University Press, 1956; and New York: Humanities Press, Inc., 1957).

Even before the appearance of *The Origin of Species,* the impact of science on sensitive personalities like Matthew Arnold and his friend Arthur Hugh Clough was apparent. Arnold in particular felt uprooted and lost, his former faith and sense of certitude practically shattered. In Arnold's own phrase (from *Stanzas from the Grande Chartreuse*), he seemed to be "wandering between two worlds, one dead,/The other powerless to be born." In poems like *Dover Beach, Empedocles on Etna,* and *Stanzas in Memory of the Author of "Obermann,"* he registered his basic pessimism. Reflecting something of the same loss of faith in the established Christian verities, Edward Fitz-

Gerald, in his celebrated translation-paraphrase of the *Rubáiyát of Omar Khayyám,* added agnosticism, fatalism and hedonism to the total picture.

The response of Alfred Tennyson to Darwinism and evolution was more direct, extensive, and affirmatively optimistic. Tennyson was an "evolutionary poet" in early works like *Maud, Idylls of the King, In Memoriam,* and *Locksley Hall,* and in poetic terms at least, anticipated *The Origin of Species.* After 1859, Tennyson retained his faith in progressive evolution, accepting and emphasizing the positive and rejecting the negative aspects of natural selection. In particular, he believed—with Darwin—that change must be slow, a view expressed in such poems as *The Making of Man, Locksley Hall Sixty Years After, By an Evolutionist,* and *De Profundis.* Also, his earlier, pre-Darwinian optimism was now somewhat tempered, and he was not as completely confident as formerly about the onward sweep of evolutionary progress.

Like Tennyson, Robert Browning accepted evolution and Darwinism, but with even greater reservations. He too was an "evolutionist" before 1859, as appears from his *Paracelsus* of 1835. Like Tennyson, he believed both before and after the publication of *The Origin of Species* in Christianity, in God and immortality, and in the progress of mankind. His particular evolutionism, rejecting the essential materialism of Darwin's writings, is best reflected in such poems as *Prince Hohenstiel-Schwangau, Fifine at the Fair,* and *Francis Furini.* And in the famous *Rabbi Ben Ezra,* Browning made his optimistic, *ad hoc* reply to the fatalism of the *Rubáiyát.*

Darwin's influence is strongly felt in the works of Algernon Swinburne, who arrived at hopeful, forward-looking conclusions from premises wholly different from Tennyson's and Browning's. Outspokenly unreligious—pagan is not too strong a word to apply to him—Swinburne in poems like *Hertha* and *Hymn of Man* preached in favor of evolutionary emancipation from the constrictions of orthodoxy. Swinburne exulted over the glorious, progressive struggle of man against the forces of supernaturalism, and his mood was challengingly optimistic.

George Meredith was similarly unorthodox in religion and affirmative in support of evolution, though he characteristically did not give vent to such orgiastic expressions as Swinburne's *Atalanta in Calydon.* Instead, he merely argued that man, though faced with the challenge of competition, will ultimately progress in spite of all obstacles. *The Thrush in February, Foresight and Patience, The Woods of Westermain,* and *Earth and Man* are some of the poems in which Meredith speaks his evolutionary views.

For Thomas Hardy, as for Arnold in an earlier day, life is bleak and hopeless. Man is caught in a meaningless competitive struggle which brings him no return. Mere purposeless coincidence and fortune rule the affairs of men. In *Hap, The Darkling Thrush, The Dynasts, The Mother Mourns,* and *A Plaint to Man,* among other works, as well as in his great novels, Hardy reveals his essential pessimism and fatalism.

There is no room here to trace the influence of Darwin on the

Victorian novel. The interested student is referred to *Darwinism in the English Novel: 1860-1910*, by Leo J. Henkin (New York: Corporate Press, Inc., 1940), for a comprehensive examination of this matter. Nor can anything be said here about the Darwinian impact on American poetry. Again, the student who wishes to pursue this subject may read with profit such a text as *Cosmic Optimism: A Study of the Interpretation of Evolution by American Poets from Emerson to Robinson*, by Frederick W. Conner (Gainesville: University of Florida Press, 1949).

There remains to add a brief bibliographical word about the influence of Darwinism on American naturalistic fiction. A collection of representative writings on naturalism is *What Was Naturalism?*, edited by Edward Stone (New York: Appleton-Century-Crofts, 1959). Two excellent studies of this subject are recommended: *American Literary Naturalism, A Divided Stream*, by Charles C. Walcutt (Minneapolis: University of Minnesota Press, 1956), and an essay by Malcolm Cowley entitled "Naturalism in American Literature," in *Evolutionary Thought in America*, edited by Stow Persons (New York: George Braziller, Inc., 1956). What the naturalists derived from Darwinism was the contention that physical, economic, and social environment, and not strength of character nor divine intervention, determines the fate of man. This has continued to be the dominant note in naturalistic fiction from Stephen Crane to Richard Wright. Man is the victim of forces over which he has little or no control. Life is grim and hard; and man, like his fellow-animals subject to fierce competition and natural laws, must struggle constantly for his physical and spiritual survival.

Three of the early important naturalistic novelists in the United States were Stephen Crane, in *Maggie: A Girl of the Streets* (1893) and *George's Mother* (1896); Frank Norris, in *Vandover and the Brute* (written in 1894-95, but published posthumously in 1914), *McTeague* (1899), and *The Octopus* (1901); and Harold Frederic, in *The Damnation of Theron Ware* (1896). Jack London, in novels like *The Call of the Wild* (1903), *The Sea-Wolf* (1904), and *Martin Eden* (1909), made his contribution to the movement, and Upton Sinclair added *The Jungle* (1906). Theodore Dreiser, perhaps the most characteristic naturalist, wrote *Sister Carrie* (1900), *Jennie Gerhardt* (1911), and *An American Tragedy* (1925), among other novels. Sherwood Anderson's short-stories in *Winesburg, Ohio* (1919) constitute a landmark in American naturalism. Sinclair Lewis was also a naturalistic writer in such a novel as *Main Street* (1920). And in more recent years, John Dos Passos has written *Manhattan Transfer* (1925) and the *U.S.A.* trilogy (1930-37); James T. Farrell, the *Studs Lonigan* trilogy (1932-35); John Steinbeck, *The Grapes of Wrath* (1939); Richard Wright, *Native Son* (1940); Willard Motley, *Knock on Any Door* (1947); and Nelson Algren, *The Man with the Golden Arm* (1949). In the 1950's a number of important World War II novels, largely naturalistic in conception, have also been published.

GLOSSARY

1. Biological and Geological Terms

Catastrophism—The theory that geological changes have occurred not slowly and gradually but suddenly, by means of catastrophes (floods, earthquakes, etc.). According to this view, each catastrophe kills off all life in its era and thus necessitates acts of special creation to replenish the earth with living creatures.

Chromosomes—Masses of protoplasm in the nuclei of cells which carry the genes, or hereditary units. Every individual of a particular species carries in the nuclei of its cells chromosomes of a characteristic number, size, and shape. Every man, for example, carries 48 chromosomes of recognizable size and shape in each of his nucleated body cells.

Darwinism—In the general biological sense, the term that refers to all the pronouncements of Charles Darwin relating to the operation of the evolutionary process—chiefly the theories of natural selection, sexual selection, and pangenesis (Darwin's explanation of the mechanism of hereditary transmission). In the more limited biological sense, it refers to natural selection alone. In the popular biological sense, it is almost equivalent to evolution itself. And in the widest non-biological sense, it refers to competition for survival, to the "struggle for existence" and the "survival of the fittest," as in "Social Darwinism," the application of evolution and natural selection to the social sciences (see *Suggestions for Further Study*, pp. 164-166).

Discontinuous Variation—The concept of variation as proceeding not always gradually, uniformly, and imperceptibly, but by means of occasional sudden leaps or jumps, as in the case of mutations.

Eugenics—The science of improving the human race mentally and physically by selective breeding. The term was introduced by Sir Francis Galton, who is generally acknowledged as the founder of the science.

Genes—The basic units of inheritance, carried on chromosomes within the nuclei of cells. Parental genes combine to determine genetic character in offspring.

Genetics—The science that deals with the mechanism of heredity. It was developed from the laws of inheritance originally worked out by Gregor Mendel in the middle of the nineteenth century, and has been refined and systematized, principally in terms of chromosome and gene theories, by many important biologists of the present century.

Germ Cells—Those cells (the egg and sperm) that carry out the process of sexual reproduction. Like other cells of the body (collectively called the "soma") each of them contains a nucleus, which in turn contains gene-bearing chromosomes. In the view of practically all biologists, it is the specialized germ cells alone that transmit the parental genes and thus establish the genetic character of offspring.

Immutability—A term often used to support belief in "special creation" or nonevolution. It means "unchangeable," and thus connotes that living

169

forms are incapable of significant change and hence of evolving from one form to another.

Inorganic Evolution—The theory that the non-living portions of the earth—bodies of water, mountain ranges, the earth's crust and interior—have developed and changed over millions of years of geological history. This is opposed to the theory that the earth's physical properties were created spontaneously and have persisted relatively unchanged except for changes occurring during periodic geological "catastrophes" (earthquakes, floods, etc.).

Lamarckian Hypothesis (or **Theory**)—The explanation of organic evolution worked out by the French naturalist Lamarck. The two leading concepts of this theory are (1) that acquired characteristics as well as physical, inborn characteristics are inherited by offspring from their parents, and (2) that living organisms may effect changes in their physical structure in response to exercise or to the fulfilment of a need for such change—e.g., the giraffe's long neck developed as a consequence of the need to obtain food that it could not otherwise reach.

Mutation—A sudden change in the number or composition of chromosomes or in individual genes which results in a mutant offspring. This offspring differs from its parents not only in the sense that their genes have been recombined in its genetic structure, but also because their chromosomes or genes, or both, have undergone changes during the reproductive process.

Natural Selection—The theory that evolution occurs when nature in effect "selects" for survival those forms of life which can best adapt themselves to their environment and produce progeny that will inherit their physical changes. Forms of life which cannot adapt in such a way will be rejected by nature and left to perish without offspring. Nature operates in natural selection as animal and plant breeders operate in artificial selection—by selecting those forms which are to survive and those which are to die, and thus effecting the evolutionary process.

Organic Evolution—The theory that all living forms of plants and animals were not supernaturally and "specially" created at one time or at successive periods of history, but that instead they developed from form to form through a process of gradual change.

Pangenesis—Darwin's theory of the mechanism of hereditary transmission. Darwin argued that "gemmules," or hereditary units, enter the germ cells from all parts of the body. As a result, each structure of the parent will be present in the germ cells and will be transmitted to the offspring. Practically all biologists today believe that the soma, or body cells, are separate from and do not contribute to the germ cells in the process of reproduction. The body cells come from germ cells, but do not give rise to new germ cells in offspring; that is, they do not contribute to the genetic character of the offspring. Only the specialized germ cells produce new germ cells, which in turn produce body cells containing the hereditary composition of the new individual.

Quadrumana—Literally, "four-handed." A biological term applied to apes, monkeys, and other primates except man because they use both hands and feet as grasping appendages.

Saltation—Literally, "jumping." A term used to describe discontinuous or sudden variation, or mutation. The reverse of slow, gradual evolution.

Sexual Selection—A further explanation of the operation of evolution. The concept means that just as natural selection operates to produce surviving animals that are more fit than others—that is, more adaptable to their environment—so the choice of mates by female animals operates to produce individuals that are sexually more attractive than others—stronger, more beautifully colored, possessed of more attractive voices and odors. The sexually more attractive individuals will mate and produce progeny which will inherit their "secondary sexual characters," and the less attractive will die without issue; thus sexual selection will influence the evolutionary process.

Special Creation—The idea that all forms of animals and plants were "specially" created by God in the beginning of time or at successive intervals of history (after geological "catastrophes") and that these forms have either become extinct, been destroyed, or persisted relatively unchanged throughout history, but that no form has evolved into any other form.

Species—A group of varieties of living things which, in terms of its characteristics and genetic relationships, is distinguished from all other varieties.

Transmutation (or **Mutability**)—The fact or possibility of change from one form or another; the theory that living plant and animal forms are capable of change and that they have in fact evolved from form to form over millions of years of biological history.

Uniformitarianism (or **Uniformism**)—The reverse of catastrophism. This theory holds that geological changes in the past were caused by the same kinds of natural processes that cause similar changes in the present. It also maintains that most geological changes occur slowly and gradually, rather than by means of sudden catastrophes.

Variety—A homogeneous group of individuals within a particular species, distinguished from other homogeneous groups within the same species.

2. A Table of Geological Time

era	period	epoch	approximate time since beginning of each period or epoch, in millions of years
CENOZOIC	Quaternary	Recent	.01
		Pleistocene	1
	Tertiary	Pliocene	10
		Miocene	30
		Oligocene	40
		Eocene	60
		Paleocene	75
MESOZOIC		Cretaceous	135
		Jurassic	165
		Triassic	205

PALEOZOIC	Permian	230
	Carboniferous	280
	Devonian	325
	Silurian	360
	Ordovician	425
	Cambrian	500
PROTEROZOIC	Pre-Cambrian	1000
ARCHEOZOIC	Pre-Cambrian	1500

(Some geologists estimate that the earth existed for as many as 1500 million years before the Archeozoic era, making its age at least three billion years.)

3. Contributors to *Darwin and His Critics*

Louis Agassiz—(1807-1873), Swiss-born American physician, zoologist, and geologist. He studied under Cuvier in Paris and later came to the United States. In 1848 he became professor of zoology and geology at Harvard University, and wrote and lectured extensively. He was the principal and most persistent opponent of Darwinism in America.

William Bateson—(1861-1926), English naturalist, professor of biology at Cambridge University. He was important primarily for developing the concept of discontinuous variation and hence for anticipating the theory of mutation. He republished and wrote about Mendel's laws of heredity.

Samuel Butler—(1835-1902), English novelist and miscellaneous writer. In 1872 he published his Utopian romance, *Erewhon; or, Over the Range,* which in part satirized Darwinism. In 1903 his autobiographical novel, *The Way of All Flesh,* appeared posthumously. A firm believer in the Lamarckian version of organic evolution, he was perhaps Darwin's most personal and most articulate opponent.

Charles Robert Darwin—(1809-1882), English naturalist, co-formulator of the theory of natural selection. After long study and exhaustive research, he became a confirmed transmutationist and worked out his theory to account for the operation of organic evolution.

Sir John William Dawson—(1820-1899), Canadian geologist and educator. From 1855 to 1893 he was principal of McGill University and professor of geology. He was a pioneer in the field of paleobotany. He was knighted in 1884.

Sir Ronald A. Fisher—(1890-   ), English biologist. Sir Ronald is one of the world's leading biometricians, or mathematical biologists. He was knighted in 1952.

Asa Gray—(1810-1888), American botanist and professor of botany at Harvard University from 1842. Gray was Darwin's earliest and most influential supporter in the United States.

Ernst Heinrich Haeckel—(1834-1919), German biologist, professor of zoology at the University of Jena from 1862 to 1909. He helped win support for

Darwinism in Germany. He is particularly remembered for his theory of recapitulation, an idea that gives support to organic evolution.

Sir Joseph Dalton Hooker—(1817-1911), English botanist, one of Darwin's closest friends and earliest supporters. He was knighted in 1877.

Sir Julian Huxley—(1887-   ), English biologist, grandson of Thomas Henry Huxley and brother of novelist Aldous Huxley. Sir Julian is one of the world's leading biologists. He has lectured and taught widely, and has written many books and articles on evolution and related matters. From 1946 to 1948 he was the director general of the United Nations Educational, Scientific, and Cultural Organization (UNESCO). He was knighted in 1958.

Thomas Henry Huxley—(1825-1895), English biologist. A close friend of Darwin and an early champion of Darwinism, he was an eminent scientist and a skillful writer and lecturer in his own right. He has become identified in history as the principal antagonist for organic evolution and, although with reservations, for natural selection.

Sir Charles Lyell—(1797-1875), English geologist. Lyell was the third of those scientists (the other two were Thomas H. Huxley and Joseph D. Hooker) whom Darwin depended upon primarily for winning acceptance of his theory of natural selection. Lyell defended Darwin and gave the theory provisional approval, although he was never quite willing to endorse it completely. His work influenced the development of Darwin's evolutionary thought, principally because of his espousal of the theory of uniformitarianism. He was knighted in 1848.

St. George Jackson Mivart—(1827-1900), English anatomist and biologist. He was an evolutionist but an opponent of Darwinism. A Roman Catholic convert, before his death Mivart was excommunicated for some of his writings dealing with the relationship between religion and science.

Thomas Hunt Morgan—(1866-1945), American zoologist and geneticist. He was a professor of experimental zoology at Columbia University from 1904 to 1928. In 1933 he was awarded the Nobel Prize in Physiology and Medicine for his research into the behavior of genes and chromosomes. Morgan developed the use of the fruit fly, *Drosophila,* as the standard subject for laboratory study of genetics.

Sir Richard Owen—(1804-1892), English zoologist and comparative anatomist, one of the most distinguished scientists of his time. He was unshaken in his opposition to Darwinism. He was knighted in 1884.

George John Romanes—(1848-1894), Canadian-born English biologist. He was a friend and supporter of Darwin and wrote widely on evolution. He lectured at the University of Edinburgh and at the Royal Institute, London, and in 1891 established the annual Romanes Lectures at Oxford University.

Adam Sedgwick—(1785-1873), English geologist, professor of geology at Cambridge University from 1818. He made many important contributions to the field of geology.

George Bernard Shaw—(1856-1950), Irish-born British dramatist, Shaw is one of the chief figures in the history of world drama. He also wrote five novels and a great deal of nonfiction, chiefly in the form of prefaces to his plays. Perhaps because of his admiration for Samuel Butler, he opposed Darwinism. In 1925 he was awarded the Nobel Prize in Literature.

Herbert Spencer—(1820-1903), English philosopher. One of the most prolific, versatile, and influential thinkers and writers of the nineteenth century, Spencer spread evolutionary and Darwinian theories into fields other than biology, particularly into the social sciences.

Hugo de Vries—(1848-1935), Dutch botanist, best known for his research on discontinuous variation and for his formulation of the theory of mutation. He was one of the three botanists (the other two were Karl Correns and Erich von Tschermak-Seysenegg) who in 1900 independently rediscovered Mendel's laws of heredity. From 1881 to 1918 he was a professor of botany at the University of Amsterdam.

Alfred Russel Wallace—(1823-1913), English naturalist, the co-formulator of the theory of natural selection. Although he continued to support the theory, in his later writings he expressed views that differed somewhat from Darwin's.

August Weismann—(1834-1914), German biologist, professor of zoology at the University of Freiburg from 1866 to 1912. He was responsible for "Weismannism," or the theory of the unbroken continuity of the germ cells in the process of heredity. He used this theory to argue against the Neo-Lamarckians and their belief in the transmission of acquired characteristics.

Samuel Wilberforce—(1805-1873), English clergyman, writer, and lecturer. In 1845 he became bishop of Oxford. He was a particularly effective orator, but his opponents, irked by his somewhat unctuous manner, supplied him with the undignified sobriquet of "Soapy Sam."

4. Other Important Persons Mentioned in *Darwin and His Critics*

William Jennings Bryan—(1860-1925), lawyer and statesman. He was three times the unsuccessful Democratic candidate for President of the United States. He served as Secretary of State in the cabinet of President Woodrow Wilson. In 1925 he offered his services to the prosecution in the Scopes evolution trial in Dayton, Tennessee, and engaged in bitter debate there with Clarence Darrow, one of the counsel for the defense.

George Louis Leclerc, Comte de Buffon—(1707-1788), French naturalist. One of the important evolutionist precursors of Darwin.

Robert Chambers—(1802-1871), Scottish author and publisher. In 1844 he published his *Vestiges of the Natural History of Creation* anonymously. He argued in support of transmutation of species, and thus anticipated Darwin.

Georges Léopold Chrétien Frédéric Dagobert, Baron Cuvier—(1769-1832), French zoologist and geologist. He was the champion of the theory of catastrophism and the enemy of uniformitarianism.

Clarence Darrow—(1857-1938), American defense lawyer who volunteered to serve without fee as one of the defense counsel in the Scopes evolution trial of 1925 in Dayton, Tennessee. His principal antagonist during that trial was William Jennings Bryan, one of the counsel for the prosecution.

Erasmus Darwin—(1731-1802), English physician, scientist, and poet, Charles Darwin's grandfather. In his long poem, *Zoonomia* (1794-1796), he anticipated the evolutionary views of his grandson.

Sir Francis Galton—(1822-1911), English scientist, grandson of Erasmus Darwin and hence Charles Darwin's first cousin. He founded the science of eugenics and gave it its name. He was knighted in 1909.

Jean Baptiste Pierre Antoine de Monet, Chevalier de Lamarck—(1744-1829), French naturalist and unquestionably Darwin's most important predecessor as an evolutionist. He supported organic evolution and developed a body of theory, referred to collectively as Lamarckism, to explain its operation.

Carolus Linnaeus (Latin form of his real name, **Carl von Linné**)—(1707-1778), Swedish botanist, founder of systematic botany and originator of the binomial method of designating plants and animals—by genus and species.

Thomas Malthus—(1766-1834), English economist and sociologist. In his *An Essay on the Principle of Population* (published originally in 1798), he contended that while population grows at a geometrical rate, the means of subsistence for that population grows at a mere arithmetic rate. Unless war, famine, and disease operate to reduce the population, or unless man exercises "moral restraint" in producing offspring, the result will be widespread hunger and poverty. According to his own testimony, Darwin began working out his theory of natural selection after reading Malthus.

Gregor Johann Mendel—(1822-1884), Austrian monk and botanist. In his work entitled, in English translation, *Experiments in Plant Hybridization* (1866), he spelled out the principles of what later became the science of genetics.

William Paley—(1743-1805), English theologian, who published *Natural Theology: or, Evidences of the Existence and Attributes of the Deity, Collected from the Appearances of Nature* (1802), in which he devised an ingenious and popular demonstration of the existence of God.

INDEX